CHANCE AND PROVIDENCE

CHANCE
AND
PROVIDENCE

God's Action in a World
Governed by Scientific Law

WILLIAM G. POLLARD

CHARLES SCRIBNER'S SONS *New York*

To my wife

MARCELLA

through whom, by the providence of God,
this previously inaccessible
range of reality
has been opened to me

PREFACE

It is a most difficult thing for the scientifically trained mind to conceive how God could act in His world. From the standpoint of science every event is the product of empirically ascertainable antecedents with which it is causally related. To speak of an event as an act of God, or to say that it happened because God willed that it should, seems a violation of the whole spirit of science. The scientifically trained man will counter such an assertion with cogent and apparently inescapable arguments. He will assert that the cause of any event is subject to scientific investigation and experimental verification. He will point to numerous examples of phenomena which in past ages were universally regarded as divinely caused but which are now understood quite adequately and even simply in terms of known scientific laws. He will insist that the only proper attitude is one of suspended judgment until the matter has been properly studied. He will further require that every suggested explanation, including the possibility of God's action, be clearly labeled as hypothetical until it has been experimentally verified. Since no one can imagine how to produce an experimental verification of the Divine activity, this usually settles the matter. For it is certainly both proper and necessary to maintain a clear distinction between what we understand and what still remains to be cleared up. This, however, we can only do by reserving judgment

7

until our growing store of scientific knowledges catches up with the situation in question.

In my own experience of coming into the Christian ministry from an already established career as a physicist, this question has been the most crucial of all. To me it seems a much more difficult and decisive question than that of the existence of God. I found extraordinary difficulty, when I thought about events in scientific terms, in imagining any kind of loophole through which God could influence them. True enough, by the time this problem arose with me I had also learned to think about events in Biblical terms as well. The thing that made the problem so acute with me was the discovery that for me these terms had become just as real and solidly based as the scientific terms of thought to which I had been so long accustomed. There was no escaping the sense I had of the reality of God's grace and providence, of His judgment and redeeming power in life and history which lies at the core of the Biblical understanding. This reality could no more be denied than the reality of the world of electrons, atoms, and physical law which I knew in physics. Yet when I tried to put these two worlds together their apparent incompatibility baffled me. It seemed as though I could not find any way in which to make them coalesce so as to form one world, encompassing a single reality. Such a situation is of course intolerable. I had come to know two realities, each all encompassing and of universal scope, which were so firmly and broadly rooted in my own experience that it was unthinkable to give up or deny either of them. Yet at the same time I could not see any point in the world as it is known in physics at which the hand of God could be thrust in and providence, as it is known Biblically, actually exercised.

This book represents the result of a period of some eight years of wrestling with this problem. There were several false starts and several periods of suspended progress while I awaited some new clue or fresh insight. At first I tried to approach it by formulating limitations on science in such a way that at least some residual domain of experience might be identified which was inaccessible to science and within which the divine action could take place. At a later stage this approach became redirected to a concentration on the Bohr Principle of Complementarity as a possible avenue of escape from my dilemma. My efforts along this line of thought culminated in two papers which were published in 1952 under the titles "New Concepts for the Social Sciences Suggested by Modern Physics"* and "The Significance of Complementarity for the Life Sciences."** The ideas developed in these two papers are reflected here in the discussion of complementarity in Chapter V.

For a while I had to leave the problem in this interim stage of its resolution even though I was not entirely happy with it or convinced by it. Then I ran across two ideas which together represented significant clues to the resolution of the problem developed here. The first of these is a distinction between physical reality and historical reality which has been made and developed by my friend, Professor Henry Margenau of Yale University, in his book, *The Nature of Physical Reality,* and elsewhere. The other is the distinction between scientific and historic time which is made so cogently by Professor Carl von Weizsäcker in his book, *The History of Nature.* From the time when these two ideas came to my attention until now, the whole trend of

* *Association of American Colleges Bulletin,* vol. 38, pp. 234-245, 1952
** *American Journal of Physics,* vol. 20, pp. 281-288, 1952

my thought has been directed toward chance and accident in history and little by little the framework of this book has emerged in my thinking.

The occasion for committing myself to the, for me, extremely arduous task of setting my ideas down on paper in a coherent and orderly fashion was provided by the invitation to give the Kellogg lectures at the Episcopal Theological Seminary in February 1957. The first three and the last chapters of the present volume were delivered in their present form as the first, second, third, and fifth of these lectures. Subsequently with the kind forbearance of the publishers the material given in the fourth lecture has been extensively revised and added to so as to form two separate chapters, the fourth and fifth, of this book.

So at last I rest my case for all to see and accept or reject as they see fit. There is a distressing finality and irrevocability about congealing one's position in print in a book which all may procure and object to as they please thereafter. When I reflect on how my own ideas have grown and changed and been redirected over the past eight years, I can only wonder whether several years hence even I will agree with what has been set down here. Yet this is the risk which anyone who dares to break into print must take. There is, however, a real difference between my present condition and the years which preceded it. It is now a whole year since I first delivered these lectures, and yet I find on rereading the manuscript that the argument still makes good sense to me. I console myself with the thought that I have really and truly found the only possible way to reconcile Biblical providence and scientific causality. In the past at previous stages of my thought I had gnawing uncertainties and a realization that what I had achieved was not really an acceptable resolution of the problem. But now I feel differently. Ten years from now the idea may well be much more clearly and more forcefully expressed than it is now. But I do believe it will not even then be an essentially different idea. What I have developed here is, I think, the real clue to this baffling problem, and I am content to plant it as such for others to develop as God gives them grace to see more clearly its further implications.

W.G.P.

WASHINGTON, D.C.

THE COLLEGE OF PREACHERS

JANUARY 1958

CONTENTS

CHANCE AND PROVIDENCE

1

THE PROBLEM OF PROVIDENCE
IN CONTEMPORARY THOUGHT

Among the several key elements of the historic Christian faith which are difficult for the modern mind, there is none so remote from contemporary thought forms as the notion of providence. The central Judeo-Christian apprehension of events in individual life and in history as manifestations of the work of the living God, acting in judgment or in redemption, has lost all meaningful content. It is common to run across the statement that we stand in contrast to men of earlier centuries, most particularly in that we can no longer believe as they did in the divine guidance of history or the hand of God in events. Even more significantly such statements, however phrased, are offered axiomatically without any felt need for justification. One can count on a large measure of common agreement today that the very idea of providence is no longer tenable.

We live, of course, in a scientific age. The outlook of all of us, scientist and non-scientist alike, has been deeply and profoundly molded by science. In every area of thought and inquiry, the scientific approach to our problems dominates all other pre-scientific approaches. Time after time phenomena which had always before been baffling and mysterious have yielded to scientific analysis, and are now seen to have a quite proper and expected place in the causal network of the natural world. There has seemed to be no limit to the capacity of science to inquire into any given situation and eventually to explain it completely as the inevitable consequence of the antecedents out of which it emerged and with which it is causally connected. The patient who believes he has been providentially delivered from sickness is refuted by his physician who explains the event in terms of well-understood physiological, biochemical, and bacteriological processes whose combined operation led unfailingly in accordance with universal laws of nature to an expected result. The farmer who believes rain to have been providentially provided for his crops finds his beliefs challenged by the meteorologist who explains it in terms of the physics of the atmosphere and the movement of air masses. The joy and gratitude which earlier filled the hearts of all in contemplating the manifold provision which God has made for His creatures in grain and fruit and flower, in the good earth and green pasture, in lofty forests and buried mineral treasure, have been replaced by a sense of marvel at the achievements of man in modern electronics, chemistry, agriculture, and medicine which have showered upon us a new abundance of man-made foods, materials, and devices.

The record of the last two centuries has been one of the steady advance of science and the steady retreat of cherished ideas about the structure of the physical world and the causes of events within it; ideas which we had inherited in intimate association with the central affirmations of our Judeo-Christian tradition. In this process the place of providence in the fabric of history has gradually given place to a growing awareness of the inner causal coherences of nature herself. In place of a world which at every instant of its existence was upheld and sustained by the power of its Creator and continuously responsive in the unfolding of its history to His controlling and guiding will, we have come to think of our world instead as a vast and intricately complex mechanism unfolding inexorably in accordance with fixed and timeless laws defining and determining its behavior down to the most intimate detail. The relation between God and nature, if acknowledged at all, has been reduced to that of the *deus ex machina* who, having initially brought the world into existence and endowed it with a certain structure regulated by a complete system of scientific law, has ever since stood wholly apart from it. For a time some areas or aspects of nature remained in which the old relationship of dependence and responsiveness to God's will could be maintained. But the number and extent of such areas have steadily shrunk as the progress of science has led it successively from mechanics, to chemistry, to biology, and finally to psychology, sociology, and even to economics, politics, historiography, and jurisprudence. In the end nothing has seemed to have been reserved to the proper operation of divine providence which apparently could not equally well, or indeed even more fruitfully, be understood in terms of the inner coherences of nature herself.

Present-day tensions for the Christian

This situation has seemed to many to lead to an impasse between the traditional Judeo-Christian understanding of God, man, and nature, and the insights and understandings of modern science. For the non-religous secularist this impasse is regarded as real, and is used by him as the basis for denying the validity of the central claims of both Judaism and Christianity concerning the activity of God in human life and history in judgment and redemption to which the Bible bears witness. All of us are familiar with such attacks and with the way in which the existence of presumably adequate scientific or materialistic explanations for phenomena or events, which for the faithful are manifestations of providential action, have been used to deny the validity of such an interpretation.

What is not nearly so widely recognized, however, is the extent and gravity of this same problem for all of us who stand inside the Faith. We, just as much as our secular colleagues, have been radically affected by the new insights and understandings which have come to us from modern science. We cannot, and certainly do not wish to, close our eyes to this new knowledge and expanded world view. At the same time, we are equally firmly convinced of the truth and validity of the Judeo-Christian witness to the God who acts in historic events. This conviction we have not only on the basis of the whole sequence of events in history to which the Bible and the Church bear witness, but on the basis of our own present experience of the Christian life in prayer and sacrament. Both of these realities of our contemporary existence are equally vivid for us, and we cannot deny either in the interest of a merely rational coherence without doing violence to the facts of life as we experience it. Yet between these two domains of our life as members of the Body of Christ on the one hand, and as participants in mid-twentieth century, science-oriented culture on the other, there are real tensions. In no area are these tensions and dilemmas so sharply defined or so apparently irresolvable as in that of the providential activity of God in events here and now.

In order to exhibit this tension and its implications in a concrete way, consider the familiar versicles and responses in Evening Prayer:

> "O Lord, save the State
> And mercifully hear us when we call upon thee.
> Give peace in our time, O Lord.
> For it is thou, Lord, only, that makest us dwell in safety."

The twentieth-century worshipper who joins in these supplications may do so with a keen sense of the reality and validity of the relationship between God and His world which they imply. As soon, however, as he is removed from the context of worship into his everyday life in the world he may, if he thinks about it, find it extraordinarily difficult to give any meaningful content to them. Against the background of understanding of the forces which shape history and of the factors which influence the balance between war and peace which most of us have been given, it is likely to prove very difficult to conceive of a way in which God is in a positiion to enter into our history in such a way as effectively to *save* our country in its present dangers and dilemmas, or determine the present issue between peace and war. Turning to contemporary works in history, economics, sociology, or political science, we shall find no view which in any way supports our response that it is our Lord *only,* who makes it possible for us to dwell in safety. The two sources of our inner convictions and understandings are clearly poles apart. Yet those within the fold of the Church today must live by the validity of both, without for the most part possessing any commonly shared rational way of seeing *how* they could both be true at the same time.

Purpose and viewpoint of the book

The purpose of these chapters is to explore this dilemma and to inquire into the possibilities for its meaningful resolution. This, however, will be done in terms of the questions and problems which naturally arise with those who stand firmly within the Judeo-Christian cultural heritage. It will, therefore, be assumed throughout that the literature of this tradition, the Bible, bears true witness to the actual acts of the living God in real historical events. The inquiry to be undertaken acquires as a result a certain fixed foundation or vantage point from which to investigate the difficult problems which present themselves. This vantage point is one from which the entire space-time universe is seen as a created affair, brought into being by a pure act of will of its divine Author, and ever since then the object, in its minutest detail, of His sustaining providence and mysterious purpose. From this vantage point it *cannot* be a coldly impersonal or darkly inscrutable universe, nor can it be a merely naturalistic or mechanical affair containing within itself all that is required for its own existence, and properties, and history. In other words, the world as conceived here will be from the outset and throughout a strictly Biblical world.

Another way to put this is that the point of view which will be adopted here is theological, in the strict sense of the word, rather than apologetic. Theology proper is a rational inquiry by the faithful for the faithful. In St. Augustine's great phrase, it is "the faith seeking to understand itself." Apologetics, on the other hand, is a discourse between the faithful and the outside world which seeks to defend the integrity and validity of the faith in terms which will be meaningful to those who do not share it. The present treatment of the subject of providence will not be concerned, except incidentally and occasionally, with making the Biblical point of view intelligible or acceptable to the secular world. Rather, it will concern itself with the peculiar problems and paradoxes which those who share this point of view experience when confronted by the evidently valid insights of secular knowledge.

The *a priori* adoption of a basic Biblical vantage point for the conduct of this inquiry does not, however, imply, as might be supposed, a correspondingly weakened or disparaging view of the validity of secular or scientific knowledge. The quest of modern science has led mankind into many hitherto unsuspected pathways of understanding, vastly expanded the range of human experience, and led to truly marvelous increases in our understanding of the hidden structure of things. The achievement of the magnificent edifice of modern science is one of the finest fruits of the human spirit which it would be not only fruitless, but, I believe, also downright irreverent, to disparage. We must instead accept it at full value, rejoicing in the marvel and beauty of it, and acknowledging throughout the essential validity which it undoubtedly possesses. Thus we shall be committed at the outset to the essential validity and reality of both the historic revelation of the living God to which the Bible and the Church together bear witness and at the same time to the essential validity of the whole structure of modern science. To both we shall endeavor to maintain an unyielding loyalty, limiting ourselves to an attempt to understand how it can be that both can be simultaneously valid and true within one and the same world.

Scientific determinism

Let us begin our inquiry by attempting to identify and formulate clearly the major problems which must be faced and adequately solved if we are to come out with a satisfactory resolution of the tensions created by the attempt to hold fully to both of these primary loyalties. Clearly the most important of these is the determinism and thoroughgoing causality which has seemed to be a fundamental and inescapable property of science. Wherever science has turned its investigative techniques, it has seemed essential to its approach to require that any phenomenon which is observed to occur must have happened the way it did because a combination of all the natural laws operative in the situation required that particular outcome and no other. In physics, chemistry, astronomy, geology, biology, biochemistry, physiology, genetics, psychology, sociology, economics—indeed in every conceivable field of investigation open to scientific study—this has seemed to many to be of the very essence of science itself. Certainly to assert the opposite, namely, that some phenomena in these several fields can be observed to happen which are not a necessary outgrowth of the operation of natural law in the situation which produced them, would seem to offer a decisive block to scientific understanding in that field and to frustrate the further application of science to it. Yet up to now

24

the unanimous witness of scientists working in all of these fields is that no such phenomena have ever been observed. Many observable phenomena in every field, to be sure, are known for which natural causes have not yet been identified, and which are, therefore, not yet understood. But nowhere is there any evidence that there are any which inherently cannot ultimately be understood in that way. Moreover, the impressive list of past triumphs of scientific investigation in each field in gaining understanding of one previously baffling phenomenon after another is sound basis for confidence in the indefinite continuation of such successes among all other phenomena which at this stage are still obscure.

Now if this characteristic is indeed so fundamental to science and scientific knowledge that an alternative to it cannot even be conceived which would not at the same time undermine the integrity and validity of science, then it must follow that insofar as science is true the whole universe must indeed really be a vast and intricate mechanism which at any moment has only one possible outcome. Given the universe with the particular structure and composition which science has disclosed our universe to have, and regulated by the particular set of universal laws which science has disclosed to be operative within it, then it must seem to follow that the state into which it goes from any previous state must be fixed by the requirement that these laws be followed within the given structure.

Providence by intervention

It will be my purpose in the next chapter to show that this view of the essential nature of science is incorrect and that the whole body of scientific knowledge presently achieved does not in fact have this character at all. For the moment, however, let us accept it as an essential attribute of science, as many certainly still suppose it to be, and turn to an examination of the way in which providence could be operative in such a universe. Clearly, in such a case, divine influence on the course of events must come by way of intervention. Every act of God in history must be an act contrary to nature, entering into the flow of things from the outside, and redirecting it so that a new sequence of events takes place which is different from that which would have happened naturally. This inevitably places God and nature in opposition to each other in the sense that they represent two alternative causative agents. Nature in this view is quite capable of taking care of things herself and would do so in a perfectly definite and determinate manner if no intervention occurred. God on His part could, if He so willed, stand completely apart from nature and so let history unfold along its predetermined course in accordance with the special structure and laws with which He had endowed the world at its creation. In that case there would, of course, be no such thing as providence. In order, then, for providence to be a real element of the world and not merely an illusory aspect of it, it is necessary in this view that there be a continuous sequence of divine interventions modifying and changing the natural course of events.

Karl Heim in his book, *Transformations of the Scientific World View,* has used the analogy of a newspaper printing press for this type of relationship between God and nature. Once an edition of the newspaper is made up, the type is set in the presses and everything which will appear on the printed copies which emerge from the press is completely predetermined. However, the editor can at any time he wishes stop the presses and insert new type for new copy in place of an earlier story. Once the presses are started again the new material appears on the subsequent copies in place of the old.

The difficulty with such a view of providence is its almost wholly non-Biblical character. The idea of a nature which was capable of running along on her own course apart from God even for a short time is entirely foreign to Biblical thought. Providence in the Bible is a continuous relationship of dependence of both man and nature on God of such mutuality and intimacy that the latter could not continue at all if ever the relationship were broken. How, for example, can we reconcile the God whose praises are sung in the following passages from the Psalms with this kind of intervention in an otherwise self-sufficient creation:

> "Thou shalt show us wonderful things in thy righteousness, O God of our salvation; thou that art the hope of all the ends of the earth, and of them that remain in the broad sea.
>
> "Who in his strength setteth fast the mountains, and is girded about with power.
>
> "Who stilleth the raging of the sea, and the noise of his waves, and the madness of the peoples."
>
> Psalm 65:5-7 (Prayer Book)

> "For the Lord is a great God; and a great King above all gods.
>
> "In his hand are all the corners of the earth; and the strength of the hills is his also.
>
> "The sea is his and he made it; and his hands prepared the dry land."
>
> Psalm 95:3-5

"O Lord how manifold are thy works! in wisdom hast thou made them all; the earth is full of thy riches.

"So is the great wide sea also; wherein are things creeping innumerable, both small and great beasts.

"These wait all upon thee, that thou mayest give them meat in due season.

"When thou givest it them, they gather it; and when thou openest thy hand, they are filled with good.

"When thou hidest thy face, they are troubled: when thou takest away their breath, they die, and are turned again to their dust.

"When thou lettest thy breath go forth, they shall be made; and thou shalt renew the face of the earth.

"The glorious majesty of the Lord shall endure for ever; the Lord shall rejoice in his works."

Psalm 104:24, 25, 27-31

But it is not only in its failure to express the spirit and all pervading character of the Judeo-Christian idea of providence that the intervention type of divine activity is unsatisfactory. On the other side of our dilemma, it is just as unsatisfactory to the whole spirit and point of view of science. For when we consider the whole intricate fabric of the natural world as modern science has revealed it to us, with its beautifully ordered structure, then the whole notion of acts of intervention from the outside seems discordant and out of keeping with its inherent beauty. It is like seeing a great actor stop in the midst of a magnificent performance to pick up a line from a prompter, or a master craftsman tampering awkwardly with an otherwise perfect creation. Anyone who has had the privilege of having the whole marvelous structure of mathematical physics unfolded before his imagination and experienced the thrill of it cannot fail but find the thought of such intervention shocking. Not only does it seem to negate the integrity and essential unity of the entire structure, but nowhere in the whole range of the varied and extensive empirical support which undergirds the structure can he find any scrap of evidence for any such intervention having occurred.

The analogy of the tended machine

It is clear, therefore, that any attempt along those lines to make our Christian sense of the providence of God cohere with our scientific understanding of the nature of the world must do radical violence to both. Instead of clarifying our understanding it only succeeds in dimming the vision of reality which either vantage point is capable of providing for us. In this circumstance we are constrained to search for some alternative way out of our dilemma which may offer promise of a closer alliance between our two vantage points. One such alternative has been suggested by J. V. Langmead Casserley in a discussion of the machine-like model of the world of mechanistic science which we have been considering:

> "We know of no machines which once created require no further attention. On the contrary, machines as we know them must be continually serviced and fed. We feed coal and water to our steam engines; we lubricate and refuel our automobiles. Our machines require our constant attention, not merely because they are imperfect and often operate badly, but because it is part of their essential nature to require our attention, so that only if they are given special care can they operate in accordance with

the intentions of their designers. No, if we are to take the mechanistic analogy seriously, it requires, not merely the remote, indifferent God of the deists, who creates but does not provide, but the infinitely concerned, responsibility bearing God of the Bible, to whom must be attributed not only the act of creation but also the infinite activities of providence."[1]

This way of resolving our problem does indeed suggest a relationship between God and His creation which is much closer to the spirit of the Biblical view than the other. But on the side of science it is very difficult to employ such an analogy in a very fruitful or helpful way. In specific processes for which scientific explanations are available, such as the motion of the planets around the sun, a chemical reaction, or a bacterial invasion of the human body, it is difficult to see just how the suggested care or provision of the mechanism enters into the process. With respect also to the whole theoretical structure of modern physics about which we have already spoken, it does not seem to be really analogous to the kind of world which is represented by that structure. What the Christian needs is some way of seeing how it can be that God's providential care is operating or even has room to operate in specific and concrete situations. So long as the scientist seems to be able to account in principle for all the elements making up the particular situation in terms of the causal network which produced it, he is unable to give any content to the conviction he has when, thinking Biblically about the same situation, he concludes that it was providential. This need, however, is not met at all by an analogy which only suggests that the universe as a whole requires the constant care and attention of its Maker to keep it running in the way it is intended

---

[1] Casserley, J. V. Langmead, *Graceful Reason,* Seabury Press, 1954, p. 79.

to run. Actually, as Professor Casserley points out, the chief difficulty with this analogy is quite simply that the physical universe is not really anything like a machine.

Providential and non-providential domains

The analogy of the tended machine is ingenious and interesting but, even apart from its theoretical difficulties, it is not a pattern of thought which is actually employed in practice by Christian people when they attempt to organize and understand their experience of providence. A second alternative which we will now consider is, on the other hand, one which is characteristic of the way in which large numbers of Christians do in practice resolve the problem in their own thinking. This alternative consists in dividing creation into two domains with the inanimate physical universe in one, and the individual human person in the other. The remainder of creation then falls between in such a way that some portion of it belongs to one domain and the rest to the other but with the boundary line between them not clearly defined. The first domain of physical nature is then considered to be wholly determined and to be proceeding inexorably under its own power along the course which scientific law requires that it follow. Providence is then strictly confined to the second domain of which man is a part. Only this portion of creation is the object of His providential care and mercy, and only within it does God act in redemption or in judgment.

There are many Christians today for whom religion is an almost exclusively individual affair, a private matter between each man and his God. It is only in the inner life of the individual spirit that God's action on behalf of man is evident. Prayer, too, is private and individual, a dialogue between the self and God which has for its object, in addition to the self, at most other persons each of whom has the same private subjective relationship to God. Beyond this, the affairs of peoples and nations, of institutions and communities, of business and politics and history, are all "outside" and apart from the religious life. They are simply what men make them. God is not thought of as involved in any direct or determining way in what happens to them. There, within the limitations imposed by natural, geographic, and economic factors, men apply their intelligence and ingenuity in decision, action, and accomplishment. This and only this is the stuff which enters into the fate of institutions and states, and makes up the fabric of history. God is assumed to remain wholly aloof from this province, leaving its development wholly in the hands of natural forces and human wills; just as the secular historians, sociologists, and management specialists tell us that it operates. He confines Himself to a concern for you and me alone, for our goodness and badness, our conversion and faith, our action and inaction.

This is admittedly an extreme position in this alternative solution of the problem of providence, but it is, nevertheless, a not-too-uncommon one. Other positions may be identified which include wider and wider areas in the domain with which God is directly concerned and within which He acts. For some this domain would include the family and the parish. For others it would be extended to include other secular institutions, whole communities, and even peoples and nations. It can in some cases include all living things, leaving only inanimate nature to the rule of scientific law. But, in whatever way the boundary line may be drawn, the principle remains the same. Creation is divided into two portions, one of which operates strictly in accordance with natural law, while the other is the object of God's continuous care and attention and is alone responsive to His will.

From the standpoint of science the difficulty with this alternative is that the boundary which it must introduce has no inherent justification in terms of the nature of things as science understands it. It is only possible because of the relatively primitive stage of the human sciences compared to the physical sciences. In the former the issue between providence and determinism is not nearly so sharply drawn as in the latter, and the Biblical idea of the relationship between God and His creation is correspondingly easier to maintain in the context of modern thought. This, however, is critically dependent on the present state of our knowledge, and the suspicion, therefore, always lurks in the background that new knowledge may at any time radically change the situation. The boundary between the two domains is indeed very sensitive to the progress of science and has had to be moved time and again in the past with each new discovery or forward step in scientific understanding. A division of the world into two domains whose boundary is never very clear and always shifting under the impact of new knowledge is not a very reliable foundation on which to build.

From the standpoint of the historic Christian faith, however, there are equally cogent objections to this alternative. Place it against the cosmic magnificence of the prologue to St. John's Gospel and it pales into insignificance. It clearly fails to do justice to the total involvement of all creation, animate and inanimate, in its dependence on the power of the living God which the passages from the Psalms previously quoted express. When St. Paul speaks of the "whole creation groaning in travail together," he is expressing a fundamental aspect of the relation between man and nature and of both to God as revealed in Christ. We cannot divide creation with respect to providence without seriously weakening the force and power of the central Christian drama which is the very center of our faith. Consider, for example, the following passage from Colossians in the light of such a division:

> "In him all things were created, in heaven and on earth, visible and invisible, whether thrones or dominions or principalities or authorities—all things were created through him and for him. He is before all things, and in him all things hold together. He is the head of the body, the church; he is the beginning, the first-born from the dead, that in everything he might be pre-ëminent. For in him all the fullness of God was pleased to dwell, and through him to reconcile to himself all things, whether on earth or in heaven, making peace by the blood of his cross."
>
> (1:16-20)

The deficiencies of a division of creation into providential and non-providential domains become especially evident when we consider the status of the pre-human history of the universe. The truly remarkable sequence of events beginning with the creation of the universe five to ten billion years ago and leading up to the first appearance of man on this planet forms a story of great forward moving power full of meaning and seemingly charged with destiny. A brief account of this story as it has been reconstructed according to one of the contemporary theories of cosmology has been given in my Faculty Paper, "The Cosmic Drama."[1] We can scarcely as Christians remain true to the fullness of our Judeo-Christian heritage and still deny to this whole

---

[1] Published by the National Council, 281 Fourth Ave., New York.

major chapter of the history of nature the purposive activity and providential guidance of Almighty God. Yet this is just what the segregation of the world into providential and non-providential domains forces upon us. Certainly any of the possible ways of drawing the boundary line between them which we have considered would leave practically nothing to providence during the long stretches of history when there were no human beings at all in the world.

In the next chapter I will begin the presentation for your consideration of a quite different approach to this problem which seems to me to offer an entirely adequate solution of it. Under it, as we shall attempt to show, there can emerge again in all of its ancient power the fullness of the Biblical response to the living God who is ever active in the whole of His creation sustaining, providing, judging, and redeeming all things, both in heaven and in earth, in accordance with the mysterious and hidden purposes of His mighty will. At the same time, however, this is accomplished in such a way that the essential integrity and unity of science, both as it is now and as in principle it may become, is fully preserved. This in brief is the admittedly very ambitious task which is now proposed to be carried out in the remaining pages of this book.

2

THE CHARACTER OF TYPICAL
SCIENTIFIC KNOWLEDGE

The basis of the merger of the Biblical idea of providence with the world view of science within one and the same universe which forms the theme to be developed in this book is a relatively elementary and simple idea, and one, moreover, which is much older than science itself. It rests on the contention that in the vast majority of natural processes there are two or more alternative responses which the system involved in the process can make. If the same process is repeated a large number of times under identical conditions, the different alternatives open to it may be observed to occur with different frequencies, and one can then assign to each of them a probability of occurrence. When this is the case in any field of scientific investigation, the character of scientific description and explanation in that field is called "statistical" because it employs probabilities in place of certainties as in the familiar field of vital statistics. In these terms, the thesis on which our whole consideration of the nature of providence rests is simply that, contrary to a widespread impression even among scientists, the world is so constituted that the ultimate as well as present characteristic mode of scientific explanation in all fields is statistical.

The bearing which such a statement, if true, may or may not have on the problem of providence is a separate question of no mean dimensions in its own right. It involves many subtleties and paradoxes which will require the most thoughtful attention and disciplined consideration which we can muster. For the present, however, I wish to confine all our attention to the support of this basic contention about the nature of science. It is essential that this task be done and done well, not only because the whole burden of what I shall wish to say later about the nature of providence rests upon it, but also because the majority of people do not believe it is a true statement about the nature of the world and of science. Such a procedure has, however, its dangers for the proper achievement of my ultimate objective. These dangers arise from the assumptions which some are likely to make as we go along concerning just how I propose to make use of the points which I am taking such pains to drive home. Many, for example, will already be familiar with one or more treatments of freedom and determinism which some scientists have advanced on the basis of the Heisenberg uncertainty principle. When I, too, use this same principle in a crucially important way, some are likely to make assumptions about the train of reasoning to which I am committed and the outcome to which my thought is leading. This, however, I must ask them to avoid doing, not only because it would tend to weaken the effectiveness of the more limited objective on which I will be working at the time, but also because the application which I propose to make of the results of it is really quite different from any other applications with which I am familiar which have been made of the same results.

Statistical character of scientific knowledge

Returning to our present inquiry into the nature of scientific knowledge, let us begin by noting the extent to which the various sciences are actually statistical in nature in their present stage. Here the example of the social sciences is the one which has the widest familiarity. The role of the investigator in these sciences is to study a large number of repeated instances of behavior under similar circumstances and to express his results in terms of norms and extremes with probabilities assigned to each mode. The now famous Kinsey report is a case in point, and many other examples come to mind. Before each major holiday the National Safety Council predicts with surprising accuracy the number of traffic deaths which will occur. Population trends can be predicted with considerable accuracy. Sociological studies in the fields of crime, race relations, industrial personnel and management, juvenile delinquency, or church attendance are all of this character. The familiar area of psychological testing for intelligence, aptitudes, fitness for various tasks, and the like, all express their results in terms of norms from which occasional wide fluctuations can occur. So also with such typical psychological studies as those which have been made of the processes of conditioning and learning, as well as with special studies such as those on identical twins. In all of these cases individual instances are indeterminate, but reliable and significant conclusions of a statistical character concerning behavior in the aggregate can be had in which the results are expressed in terms of probabilities.

The biological sciences also express much of their information about the behavior of living systems in statistical terms. Important examples are to be found in genetics and in the effects of environmental factors on whole organisms. In the former case the fundamental processes of gene mutation and chromosome breakage and linkage are basically statistical in nature. Studies of these processes consist in determining normal rates for each mutant form expressed in terms of the fraction of all cell divisions in which the particular mutant appears. The effect of external factors such as temperature, radiation, oxygen supply, or added chemicals is then expressed in terms of the change produced in these normal rates of occurrence of the same mutant forms. In the other example it is necessary to recognize that individual organisms of the same type or species do not respond identically to the same changes in the environment. As a result, studies of nutritional factors, radiation effects, infectious diseases, temperature, and the like on various organisms are always carried out statistically and the results expressed in terms of probabilities.

The biological sciences do, however, provide examples of the determinate kind of scientific information to which we have become accustomed in the physical sciences. These examples are chiefly biochemical and biophysical and include such topics as the structure of proteins, enzymes, nucleic acids, and other cell components, as well as studies of processes such as the mechanism of metabolism, photosynthesis, muscular contraction, transmission of nerve impulses, and many other subjects of current biological investigation. All such cases represent, however, aspects of biology which belong in their essential features to physics and chemistry. For our present purpose they can, therefore, be discussed along with these sciences.

Chance as a measure of lack of knowledge

It is really from the physical sciences that the impression of a thoroughgoing determination of natural processes has been derived. It is, as a result, in a discussion of them that the thesis which I am endeavoring to establish will meet its most crucial test. That discussion, however, is of a different order of difficulty from that which has just been given of the social and biological sciences, and its intelligible development will require much more care and effort. Before undertaking it, however, it will be well to consider a possible point of view toward chance events and alternative modes of response which makes it possible to regard them, too, as instances of processes which are in their nature fundamentally determined and for which really no alternative possibility is open.

A simple example will help to make this clear. One of the most familiar and elementary applications of probability is in tossing a coin. Here two alternatives are available and the probability for each one is 50 per cent. What accounts for the introduction of chance into the outcome of tossing the coin is, however, the complexity and variety of the motions of the coin during each throw. One can argue that in an absolute sense, if we knew exactly the forces applied to the coin, its initial state, the forces of air resistance in transit, and the elastic properties of the surface which it strikes at the end of the toss, then we could predict with certainty the result of each throw. Thus, in this case the appearance of chance and probability is the result of a complexity of motion under varied conditions of starting and stopping combined with lack of knowledge of the complex factors involved in each instance.

The great majority of biologists and social scientists feel that the reason why their results to date are expressed in terms of probabilities is essentially the same as those applicable to the coin. The phenomena they investigate are admittedly of enormous complexity in all their details. Numerous minute, and for the most part unknown, influences and stimuli combine to determine the specific behavior of a living organism or a human being in a particular situation. If all of these could be known, together with all of the relevant laws responsible for the behavior, they would argue, then the precise behavior in individual instances could be predicted exactly, and it would be seen that the behavior in question was determined and really had no other alternative. Just as the coin is really not free to decide in a throw whether it shall land heads or tails, so, they would say, neither is a human being. If we could know everything necessary about his total hereditary and environmental make-up and all of the influences and stimuli impinging upon him in complete and accurate detail, then it is at least possible in theory to suppose that his behavior and final response would be seen to be completely determined and without genuine alternative.

Because this type of argument can be advanced and defended, it is not sufficient for our purpose merely to point out that in their present preliminary and relatively initial stages the biological and social sciences lead to a statistical description of phenomena involving chance and probability. In order to establish my primary thesis that this is a necessary characteristic of scientific knowledge dictated by the nature of things rather than merely a temporary result of inadequate information, it is clearly necessary for us to probe much deeper than we have so far delved. Nevertheless, the fact remains, regardless of the explanation which we may prefer, that the presently available scientific knowledge in these fields *is* statistical and probabilistic in form. This fact is important to my objective, and I shall frequently have occasion to have recourse to it.

The determinism of classical mechanics

The reasons for the nearly universal belief that the world uncovered by science will, whenever scientific knowledge becomes complete, be seen to be a world completely determined within itself, goes back to the early triumphs of the physical sciences. In order to appreciate and deal properly with the widespread expectation which so many have that scientific investigation in any field must ultimately narrow every apparent alternative to a single mode of response in any situation, we must go back to the initial development of what is now known as classical physics. The formulation of the laws of motion by Newton in the seventeenth century led to a rapid development of theoretical mechanics. A century later this subject emerged under the hands of Lagrange and Euler and later of Hamilton as a theoretical structure of universal scope and applicability expressed in a mathematical system of great beauty, simplicity, and rigor. At the peak of this theoretical structure were simple mathematical expressions which were asserted as universally and rigorously true and from which the precise behavior of every system from the simplest to the most complex could be derived. The sheer loftiness and majestic simplicity of the structure were such as to capture the imagination of all who were privileged to behold it and to test for themselves its invariable success in duplicating exactly the behavior of complicated systems in nature.

When a ball is thrown, it follows a smooth arching path with which we are all familiar. The laws of mechanics allow this path to be computed accurately and the position of the ball along it to be determined moment by moment during the course of its motion. In order for them to accomplish this, it is only necessary to know the point at which the ball left the thrower's hand and the speed and direction of its motion at this moment. These same laws are used in the science of ballistics to compute the trajectories of rifle bullets and artillery shells and more recently the orbits of rocket-launched satellites.

Still more striking is the fact that much more complex cases can be worked out with equal precision using the same simple laws. The solar system is an example of such a complex system. Here the earth and other planets move in various paths or orbits about the sun and as they do so, they attract each other by gravity in greater and lesser amounts as their paths bring them close together or carry them far apart. While this motion goes on the moon moves around the earth. The laws of mechanics are so formulated that this complex system can be treated under the very same laws which apply to the thrown ball. The treatment requires us to specifiy at any one instant the exact position in space of the sun, each planet, and the moon and the exact velocity, including the direction of motion, of each object at the same instant. This done, the laws are capable of telling us exactly where each member of the system will be and with what velocity it will be moving at any time in the future, say a thousand years from now; or, if we wish, they can tell us just what the configuration was at any time in the past, say at the birth of Christ. Moreover, these results could be applied in practice, as in the exact prediction of eclipses of the sun or moon, and we are all aware of the dramatic precision of such predictions.

Many applications of theoretical mechanics were made to a variety of physical systems and always, whenever the equations could be solved, the predicted results agreed exactly with the observed behavior. It was difficult to see how their complete generality and applicability could be limited. Nothing in our experience at the time even suggested a type of phenomenon to which they would not apply, and no one could even conceive of a factor in nature of such a character as to be contrary to them. The mathematician Laplace formulated this absolute and inescapable universality of the laws of classical mechanics in a particularly cogent and impressive manner. Only make available to him, said Laplace, a being of infinite computational capacity, a mathematical demon of enormously greater capacity than even the most elaborate of present-day high speed electronic computers. With such a demon at his service, he would then ask only to be told the exact position and velocity of every particle in the universe at a particular instant of time. With this information and the universal laws of mechanics, Laplace asserted that he could then have his demon use it to specify precisely what the exact state of the whole universe would be at any desired time in the future. The impossibility of supplying the required mathematical demon is, of course, no argument against the power of this conclusion. It is sufficient to know that the world is constructed in such a way as to make such a statement possible to have a complete and thoroughgoing determinism.

We need only apply Laplace's conclusion to ourselves to see its force. For, if true, it implies that our precise state, not only that of our physiology but of our nervous system as well, a week or a month or even a year hence is already determined in complete detail by the present precise state in which we find ourselves together with the present state of everyone and everything else which affects us in any way. To escape from this inexorable and rigid conclusion, it would be necessary to find some point at which the laws of mechanics would not apply, and no one at the time could advance even a suggestion as to what the nature of that flaw could be.

Reasoning such as this had a profound effect on the expectations which gave inspiration and drive to the opening up of other fields of scientific investigation. As the new fields of geology, biology, anthropology, psychology, and sociology opened up, the early investigators in them carried into their work a vision of the nature of the world as it must be constituted in all of its elements, which led them to expect with complete confidence that it should ultimately be possible to understand phenomena in their field in the same way that mathematical physics had been able to do in its field. There was nothing to suggest that there was any difference of kind between the two, only one of complexity and diversity. This expectation in the field of psychology is particularly boldly expressed in a statement by the psychologist and educator Thorndike, made in 1910:[1]

---

[1] Thorndike, Edward L., "The Contribution of Psychology to Education," *Journal of Educational Psychology*, 1910, vol. 1, p. 6.

"A complete science of psychology would tell every fact about every one's intellect and character and behavior, would tell the cause of every change in human nature, would tell the result which every educational force—every act of every person that changed any other or the agent himself—would have. It would aid us to use human beings for the world's welfare with the same surety of the result that we now have when we use falling bodies or chemical elements. In proportion as we get such a science we shall become masters of our own souls as we are now masters of heat and light. Progress toward such a science is being made."

It is expectations such as this which make the present statistical character of knowledge in psychology with its inclusion of chance and probability, choice and alternative, seem only a temporary expedient forced upon us by the complexity of the subject matter. Since the launching of these other sciences, however, physics has in the meantime undergone a radical change of such fundamental character and scope as to suggest a thoroughgoing re-examination of such expectations.

The indeterminism of quantum mechanics

The change in question arose out of the attempt to apply the hitherto unassailable structure of classical mechanics to atoms and molecules. Here for the first time it failed, and the failures which it experienced were not merely in its accuracy or degree of precision. The failures were radical and fundamental and of such a character as to require a revision in the whole underlying theoretical structure. The result was the development only some thirty years ago of a whole new theoretical structure called "quantum mechanics." During the relatively brief intervening period quantum mechanics has been applied with unfailing success to a range of phenomena exceeding by many times in quantity and variety the range of phenomena explained by classical mechanics. Its empirical support is most impressive and of great sturdiness.

It would carry us far beyond the purpose of this book and completely beyond the space limitations to attempt here an analysis of the nature of the fundamental difficulties which classical mechanics confronted in the atomic world or of the considerations which led to the development of quantum mechanics. For our purpose it will be sufficient to describe the way in which quantum mechanics goes about the solution of a problem and the terms in which its solution is given.

In our discussion of classical mechanics we spoke of the way in which it applied to the simple case of throwing a ball. If the ball being thrown were an electron or an atom and we wished to solve the problem with quantum mechanics of what would happen to it, the nature of the solution would be very different. First of all, we would need to know all possible modes of motion of a ball in the earth's gravitational field regardless of how it was thrown. This would correspond roughly to the problem of determining in classical mechanics the family of paths through space of a ball corresponding to every possible way of throwing it. Quantum mechanics gives us a way of finding this family of states of motion. Once these are known, we can then ask about the effect on the ball, or in this case the electron, of a particular impact corresponding to throwing it in a given direction with a given force acting over a given period of time. The result is surprising. Instead of having only one possible way in which the object could move in response to a given throw, all the possible modes of motion must be included and the object *may* respond in any one of them it chooses. The solution of the problem tells us for each possible way in which it could move, the probability that it would adopt that state of motion as its response to the given throw. True, the great majority of the possible motions are extremely unlikely and the probability that they will be chosen is essentially zero. But there are still a number of modes of motion for which the probabilities are not zero. If exactly the same throw were repeated a large number of times, each of these alternative responses to it would be observed to be followed by the object. When the relative number of times it moved in each particular way were collected, they would be found to coincide with the probabilities predicted in the quantum mechanical solution.

Sometimes the modes of motion given by quantum mechanics correspond closely with those given by classical mechanics. When this happens, the probability that the particular path which classical mechanics specifies will be followed comes out very large and all the others have very small probabilities of being followed. This capacity of quantum mechanics to approach a classical mechanics solution as a limit in certain cases is known as the *principle of correspondence*. It shows that classical mechanics is a special and limited case of quantum mechanics which is therefore the more general and universally applicable theoretical system. But even when it approaches the classical behavior it remains fundamentally different in spirit and approach. For it always contemplates alternative modes of behavior and invariably expresses its results in terms of the probabilities of their being adopted.

What has been said here about the problem of throwing a ball is true of every problem from the simplest and most elementary to the most complex and involved. The procedure and the terms are always the same. The solution of the problem specifies all the possible modes of motion or dynamical states of the physical system under consideration and the probabilities that each one of them will be selected in response to the given complex of forces acting upon it. Physics as a result has become statistical in its innermost core. It involves choice, alternative, chance, and probability just as do the other sciences we have described.

It is important that the full implications of this be made clear. You might, for example, feel that something other than the electron must really determine which one of the several apparent alternatives is taken in individual instances. Perhaps, you might reason, there is some as yet completely unknown structure or mechanism inside an electron which is different in different instances and would account, if known, for the particular alternative which the electron seems to choose. But insofar as quantum mechanics is true, such a possibility is not open. Any force of whatever character, known or unknown, which acts on the system can only result in changing the distribution of probabilities among alternative states. Any influence of whatever character can only make some modes of response more probable, and others less probable. It cannot alter the fundamental character of the whole theoretical structure which must by its very nature express results in terms of probabilities among alternative possibilities.

Radioactive iodine as an example of quantum mechanics

An actual example of this characteristic of quantum mechanics may be helpful at this point. There is a form of the element iodine which is radioactive and is rather widely used now in the treatment of disorders of the thyroid gland. It is in all respects chemically identical to ordinary stable iodine. A bottle of medicinal tincture of iodine, such as is used for cuts and other antiseptic purposes, made of radioactive iodine would look the same, smell the same, and feel the same as ordinary tincture of iodine. The only difference is that the nucleus or inner core of a radioactive iodine atom has four more neutrons in it than an ordinary iodine atom. This, however, opens up the possibility of an alternative physical state in which the particles making up the radioiodine nucleus could exist. The alternative state is one in which one of the neutrons has changed into a proton by the process of radioactivity. When this happens the nucleus of the radioiodine atom changes into a nucleus of an atom of the noble gas xenon.

Every radioiodine atom has open to it at every moment two alternatives. It may either remain in its present state and continue as a radioiodine atom, or it may explosively change one of its neutrons into a proton by emitting appropriate radiation and become a xenon atom. The quantum mechanical theory of this type of system is such that all that can be specified about it is the probability that it will make this choice in a given period of time. No forces, external or internal, known or unknown, can eliminate the element of choice from the picture. A sufficiently powerful force acting on the atom could only make it more or less probable that the choice would be made.

This probability is often conveniently expressed in terms of half-life. The half-life of a radioactive substance is the time required for half of an initial large number of atoms to make the choice to undergo radioactive decay. The half-life of radioiodine is eight days. This means that, if we should start with a million radioiodine atoms, eight days later 500,000 of them would at some time during the intervening period have changed radioactively into xenon atoms and the remaining 500,000 would still remain iodine atoms. During the next eight days half of the remainder, or 250,000, would undergo the change with the other half remaining iodine atoms.

The situation may be compared with the decision to marry among college freshmen. Each freshman man or woman has open the choice to remain single or to marry. Making use of already available methods, a sociologist, after collecting necessary data, could undoubtedly establish a half-life for marriage in the freshman class of a given college. This half-life might, for example, turn out to be say five years. If so, one could predict with reasonable certainty that at the end of five years half of the class which had started as freshmen together would be married and the other half would still be single. With respect to any individual freshman, however, no prediction at all could be made other than a knowledge of the probability of marriage characteristic of the whole group. So, too, in the case of the radioiodine atom. If we were to concentrate on one particular radioiodine atom, there would be no way whatever of telling when it might decide to change into xenon. This might happen in the next ten minutes, but it could equally well be delayed for the next ten years.

The Heisenberg indeterminacy principle

The basic characteristic of atomic and molecular phenomena which forced the transformation of classical mechanics into quantum mechanics was formulated by the German physicist,

Werner Heisenberg, in his now famous *principle of indeterminacy*. There is a universal indeterminacy measured by a universal constant of nature (Planck's constant, $h = 6.63 \times 10^{-27}$ erg-sec) to which all objects are subject regardless of their nature. For very small objects such as an electron or an atom, this indeterminacy becomes decisive and makes it impossible to specify both their position and their velocity simultaneously with precision. If either one is precisely known, then the other will be wholly indeterminate. Thus Laplace's demon, no matter how clever he might have been, could not even have begun his calculations. If we gave him the exact position of every particle in the universe at a given moment, neither he nor we could have any information at all about their velocities, and vice versa. The Heisenberg indeterminacy principle strikes at the very root of the determinism of classical mechanics and undermines its very foundations.

We must, however, proceed with great caution in drawing conclusions from the statistical character of quantum mechanics and the existence of the indeterminacy principle. There are, I believe, valid conclusions of substantial weight and significance to be drawn from all this which have a very real and vital bearing on the problem of providence. But they are not the conclusions which may seem tempting at first sight. Some have, for example, seen in the Heisenberg indeterminacy principle the basis for human freedom of the will. No such argument will, however, form any part of the thesis to be developed here. Indeed, I have grave doubts that there is any relationship at all between them. I cannot see how the existence of random chance fluctuations in the electrons, atoms, and molecules of which I am constituted can in any way contribute to an understanding of my subjective experience of my own freedom. The indeterminacies of quantum mechanics can lead only to the introduction of pure chance as in the flipping of a coin. No scheme it seems to me of introducing chance and randomness into the elements of the nervous system can be a foundation out of which an explanation of human freedom could ultimately emerge.

The use of the word "indeterminacy" is likely in itself to carry connotations about quantum physics which are misleading. The impossibility which the indeterminacy principle introduces of specifying the path or orbit of an atomic particle or of predicting when an individual atom will decide to undergo radioactive decay has been taken by some as an indication that quantum mechanics is an incomplete theory as compared with classical mechanics. Yet this is not a defect or shortcoming of the theory indicative of gaps which further work is required to fill in. For quantum mechanics has demonstrated over and over an entirely adequate predictive power in the sense that any aspect of natural systems which can be observed and measured can be dealt with unequivocally by quantum mechanics. The purpose of any theory is to represent faithfully the world as it actually is constituted. There are those, like the late Albert Einstein, who feel an inner conviction that reality must ultimately prove somehow to be completely determinate, and who therefore feel that chance, alternative, and probability have no place in its description. Despite such philosophical convictions, however, the world as it is observed to be in experimental atomic physics continues to behave on a wide front, which includes a great variety of diverse phenomena, in just the way quantum mechanics expects it to behave. Whether we like it or not, it seems to be a world in which indeterminacy, alternative, and chance are real aspects of the fundamental nature of things, and not merely the consequence of our inadequate and provisional understanding.

A related question concerns the effect of quantum indeterminacies on large-scale macroscopic phenomena of our direct experience. It is important to recognize here that with rare exceptions there can be essentially no effect of this character. Large-scale phenomena involve enormous numbers of atoms and molecules all acting together. But in every case in which individual behavior is indeterminate, but the probability of alternative possibilities is known, such probabilities approach certainties when sufficiently large numbers are involved. The moment at which an individual radioiodine atom will decide to radioactively change into xenon is completely indeterminate. A dose of radioiodine administered by a physician to a patient contains, however, a hundred million billion radioiodine atoms. With such enormous numbers involved, it is possible to predict with considerable precision exactly how many atoms will have decayed radioactively at any time after administration of the dose. So it is also with the properties of substances such as melting points and boiling points, hardness, compressibility, specific heat, and the like. All such properties are the result of tremendous numbers of atoms or molecules acting together. A prediction from quantum mechanics of the probabilities governing the indeterminate behavior of individual particles becomes, with such large numbers involved, a practical certainty in the behavior of the entire group.

Because of this, the kind of indeterminacy which is found in living organisms and human beings and which results in the use of probabilities to describe results in the biological and social sciences is not in the great majority of instances to be traced back to the Heisenberg principle. Randomness among the atoms of which the systems studied in these sciences are composed has generally been converted into an invariable and dependable behavior through the numbers involved in their structure. The phenomenon of gene mutation is the only one so far known in these sciences which produces gross macroscopic effects but seems to depend directly on changes in individual molecules which in turn are governed by the Heisenberg indeterminacy principle. Elsewhere in these sciences where variability, alternatives, and probability are found, we must suppose that they arise out of as yet undefined principles or sources of indeterminacy proper to biological organisms or man as such. Such indeterminacies are probably very different from and unrelated to the Heisenberg principle appropriate to the submicroscopic world of atoms. The supposition that there may be principles of indeterminacy appropriate to systems other than atoms and molecules arises, of course, only by analogy with what we have experienced in quantum mechanics, just as Thorndike's supposition about psychology which was quoted earlier arose only by analogy with what had been experienced in classical mechanics. Yet this is, it seems to me, an especially useful and fruitful analogy, and one which, as analogies go, rests on a particularly solid and dependable foundation.

The majority of natural phenomena are statistical in character

When we survey the whole field of natural phenomena from electrons to man, giving equal weight to everything that happens, it is surprising to discover what a rare and severely limited class is formed by phenomena of the kind studied in classical physics in which only one alternative exists. Yet the recognition of this simple fact constitutes a complete about face in traditional thinking about science in general and the nature of physical reality in particular. It demands a reorientation which is very hard to come by and which in general can only be accomplished by a slow and painful intellectual process and psychological accommodation. It will be well for us to consider a few typical examples of this general observation which will help us to perceive its total scope and validity.

The subject of fluid dynamics is concerned with an understanding of the motion or flow of fluids, both liquid and gaseous. Two broad types of flow are encountered, namely, laminar or streamline flow and turbulent flow. The application of classical mechanics to streamline flow led to the development of theoretical hydrodynamics which is a very beautiful mathematical theory. Students studying this theory and responding to its elegance and scope as well as to its many triumphs, are likely to gain an impression that laminar flow is the typical form of fluid motion, with turbulent flow, to which the theory does not apply, representing a rather rare and unimportant complication on the periphery of the subject. The actual situation, however, is just the reverse of this. Fluid flow as it occurs in nature is almost invariably turbulent flow. Air movements in the atmosphere are almost all turbulent, and it is with these that meteorologists and aerodynamicists alike must deal. Industrial or chemical engineering applications involving fluid flow are almost always turbulent rather than laminar. Astronomy to an increasing extent is concerned with problems related to turbulence in interstellar gas clouds both as concerns present phenomena in such clouds and also in problems relating to the formation of galaxies and stars.

Indeed one need only note how much ingenuity was required in teaching classical hydrodynamics to produce experimental demonstrations of laminar flow to recognize the comparative rarity of the phenomenon. True streamline flow is an exceedingly fragile and delicate thing which the least disturbance is likely to break down into the chaos of turbulence.

The importance of all this to our present considerations lies in the fact that the distinction between turbulent and laminar flow is basically one between a form of motion with alternatives which must be described statistically in terms of probabilities as in quantum mechanics, and a form of motion which has only one alternative and which therefore can be described deterministically in terms of fixed paths as in classical mechanics. In streamline flow every element of the fluid moves throughout in a fixed manner corresponding to its place in the over-all pattern of steamlines. In turbulent flow every minute volume element is in a state of rapid random fluctuation in its motion. Many alternative states of motion are available and any treatment of the subject must seek to discover ways to determine the probabilities with which these states are occupied. Now, as we have seen, turbulence is the common or normal form of fluid flow with streamline flow a rare and delicate special case. This, then, means that the typical way in which fluids move gives them a choice among many possible modes of motion. There are, however, rather rare and unusual instances in which the alternatives are reduced to one. By selecting only such instances we can treat fluid flow in a thoroughly deterministic manner. But we must not forget when we do so that we have made a highly specialized selection and that the results we obtain are highly atypical of the world in general.

One additional example in another area will help to drive home this point. We have already mentioned ballistics as an example of classical mechanics. Yet no ballistic missile ever behaves with the precision and fixed determination of path which we have come to associate with classical mechanics. Great care must be exercised in shaping bullets just right and in accurately rifling the barrel of the gun from which they are to be fired in order to achieve some approximation to the precise orbits of classical mechanics. The primary reason for this is, of course, the interaction of the bullet with the air through which it passes. The air motions involved are of necessity turbulent and this makes the interactions themselves variable and indeterminate in character. As a result there is not just a single path for the bullet to follow, but a bundle of paths any one of which may be followed in particular instances.

The solar system remains the most impressive and precise example of a natural system which obeys the laws of classical mechanics. Yet even here, if we consider the system over a sufficiently long time interval, the picture we would have would be different. All the planets and the moon seem to have condensed out of a great cloud of gas and dust from which the sun also condensed. The cloud itself was undoubtedly highly turbulent while this was going on. As the condensation progressed each one continued to collect large and small chunks of matter which fell into them in the form of meteorites. Evidence of this is still to be seen on the face of the moon and traces of the process are still evident in meteorites striking the earth. Considering this history, we can see that a moving picture of the solar system covering, say four billion years of its history, with an exposure taken every million years would certainly present a very different picture from the beautifully ordered and determinate motions in fixed orbits which we have come to think of as typical.

When, therefore, we consider the character of scientific knowledge of the world in all fields of inquiry and the terms in which it is expressed, it is possible to draw certain general conclusions about the nature of the world which science is seeking to understand. Among these the conclusion of greatest impact for our present purpose concerns the role of natural law in the shaping of events. It has been typical of scientific thought in the past to think of the laws of nature as prescribing a rigid framework within which everything is constrained to happen in a single way. This, however, is not at all typical of the way in which the laws of nature are in fact and in practice applied to phenomena in all fields of scientific investigation. The case which is really typical of science is one in which the laws of nature first define several possible states which a system under consideration may occupy in full conformance to them, and, secondly, in which they determine the probabilities that in individual instances the system will choose each of those several possible states in response to a given set of forces or causes acting upon it. Thus, the typical situation is an indeterminate one involving alternatives and latitude. Only in circumstances involving large numbers of identical systems, which are subject to the same set of forces or causes, does this set of probabilities reflect actual occurrences and emerge as a pattern of actualized and predictable behavior which becomes more and more determinate as the numbers and frequencies of occurrence increase.

Among all of the sciences isolated instances can be found in which the several alternatives of the typical case are narrowed to a single possibility. In such cases the system concerned has only one way of responding to the forces acting upon it. In the history of science such instances were seized upon first for study because of their relative simplicity and ease of analysis. By such a process of selection out of the infinite variety of phenomena awaiting scientific attention, the physical sciences developed a body of natural phenomena which could be understood in terms of a very beautiful and self-consistent theoretical structure. The experience of this accomplishment led naturally to expectations of the possibility of understanding all natural phenomena in the same terms. It was inevitable, however, that as science progressed more and more phenomena of the typical type in which two or more alternatives were present would come within its field of inquiry, in spite of the inherent tendency to exclude them through the process of selecting the simplest cases for first investigation.

It is against this background of the role of natural law in the shaping of events, as it has come to be understood as typical of nature as a whole, that we shall begin in the next chapter our consideration of the manner in which divine providence may operate in the shaping of events within the framework provided for them by the laws of the natural world.

3

PROVIDENCE AS CHANCE AND ACCIDENT

Every science divides itself naturally into two branches. First there is the primary branch of the science proper which is concerned with the investigation and understanding of phenomena in its field as they occur now in our present world. It is only in the present that experiments can be designed and carried out and it is only the world as presently organized and constituted that can be observed. As soon, however, as each science assembles a sufficient body of knowledge in its field and acquires some insight into the structure of the phenomena composing it and the laws which give this structure coherence, it becomes possible to apply such knowledge to a reconstruction of past situations. Such applications give rise to a secondary branch of the science which can properly be designated as its historical branch.

Physics and astronomy together possess as their major historical branch the subject of cosmology which is concerned with the history of the universe as a whole. Physics also concerns itself with questions about the origin of the earth and other planets, radioactive dating of rocks, and the dating of archeological specimens by means of carbon-14. All these subjects belong to its historical branch. A recent problem of an historical character in chemistry is concerned with the synthesis of organic compounds out of the earth's original atmosphere of hydrogen, ammonia, methane, and water which made possible the development of life. Geology divides itself naturally into two major branches of this sort, namely, Physical Geology and Historical Geology. Biology proper is concerned with a study of living organisms and life processes as now observed in the laboratory. But it has in the subject of organic evolution a major historical branch to which it effectively applies the insights gained from genetics, physiology, embryology, and taxonomy to a reconstruction of the history of the evolution of species. Finally, psychology and sociology have their common historical branch in the field of cultural anthropology.

Now our problem of the nature of providence belongs to the field of history. It is only in retrospect that the hand of God in the shaping of events is seen and responded to. In our present situation we have hope as we place our trust in Him, but that hope and trust rest upon the witness that has been borne to us down through the ages of His mighty acts in history as well as our own recollection of His mercy, His sustaining power, and His judgment in our own personal histories. It is in history, therefore, that we must seek the key to the puzzle of providence.

Indeed we can see this already in the fact that it is out of the historical rather than the proper branches of each science that the questions about the reality or possibility of providence which science has raised have all emerged. Biological evolution with its related branches of historical geology and paleontology is, of course, the primary example of the source of such questions, but cosmology and anthropology have both made their contributions as well.

The connection between providence and chance

A primary feature which distinguishes the historical branch of a science from its proper concern with the structure and organization of observable phenomena is the dominant role which is played by chance and accident in history. In the laboratory conditions are carefully controlled and elaborate precautions taken to exclude extraneous factors in experiments. The same phenomenon can be repeated many times under the same circumstances so that relative probabilities are actualized in sufficient numbers to make their precise determination possible. But when the same phenomena are considered in their role of shaping events as they occurred in history, then there are no controls and the situation is very different. Here the most improbable is discovered to have happened and the most widely extraneous factors to have entered into the situation in a decisive manner. As a consequence of this, the language employed in the historical branch of a science will differ from that used in its proper branch. A geneticist, speaking as such in his proper field, speaks of "mutation rates," but when speaking of the role of genetics in evolution he speaks of "chance mutations." A biochemist reporting on his laboratory results speaks of enzyme activity, intermediary metabolites, and other ordered processes, but when he concerns himself with the emergence of nucleic acids or proteins in the origin of life he speaks of accidental associations and of trial and error.

It will be my purpose to defend the thesis that the key to the Biblical idea of providence, and, therefore, to providence in the form in which we as Christians perceive it, is to be found in the appearance of chance and accident in history. In supporting this thesis we will attempt to show that it is not in any way peculiar to the special kinds of questions which have been raised by modern science, but that it has always been so throughout the whole history of Israel and the Church. What Israel perceived as a mighty act of God was to other peoples only a particularly favorable combination of circumstances. What Israel called Providence, the Greek called Fortune. What to the faithful is an act of divine mercy showing forth our Lord's restorative power is for the pagan merely a piece of extraordinarily good luck. What to the faithful is a manifestation of divine judgment is to the pagan only a misfortune. So, too, in our day as we strive to give content in a world dominated by scientific categories of thought to the reality of the activity of the living God in our life and history, and to give meaning and substance to the great words we use to describe it—redemption, mercy, salvation, judgment, and the Lordship of Christ—we, too, must turn to that which our secular contemporaries recognize as chance and accident, if we are to find the key to our problem.

The openness of history

The word "history" is often restricted to the recorded history of man and therefore to be confined to the last five thousand years or so. But science has shown us that nature, too, has a history and that human history is continuous with it. It is meaningful to speak now not only of the history of man, but equally well of the history of life on the earth, or of the history of the earth itself. We are even beginning in cosmology to speak of the history of stars, of galaxies, and lately of the age and history of the entire universe. For the purpose of this discussion the word "history" will always be taken in its broadest sense to include the sequence of events so far as it can be known within the whole space-time universe from the moment of its creation some five to ten billion years ago until now. In the totality of history in this sense of the word, the history of man (which is its classical sense) is only a very small fragment.

As we saw in the first chapter, one of the central problems we face in formulating an adequate idea of providence is the widespread impression that history really, if everything relevant to it were known about it, has only one way in which it could unfold. This is naturalistic determinism, and it is based on the impression that the laws of nature allow only one alternative in each situation. But this we have seen to be a misconception, since the typical situation in science is one in which several alternatives are open in each natural process. In terms of this more typical view of science, history takes on a quite different aspect. Its possibilities and potentialities are opened up enormously. At every moment the countless myriad of diverse elements which go to make up and define the state of the universe at that instant have each their own separate choices to make among the alternative paths of response open to them. Each must, under the inexorable requirement of temporal existence to which all creation is subject, choose one path and take it, foregoing the other alternatives of that moment forever. The sum total of all these choices advances history one step further along its path, at which another set of alternatives presents itself with another set of choices. So it has gone moment by moment, step by step, for five or ten billion years. Each stage has been a springboard for the next with many possible directions in which the jump could be made. History is like a vast and intricate maze through which creation has threaded its way. Every turning point in it contributed its bit to the selection of the pathway which history has actualized, while at the same time abandoning forever other pathways which, had they been taken, would have led to a very different history. So far as the laws of nature and the structure of things in space and time are concerned, the universe *could* have had many histories other than the one it has had. At the same time, however, it is equally true, under the stern requirements of the necessity of choice in temporal existence, that it *can* have only one of these histories. All the others must be abandoned and remain forever unknown and unknowable, lost in the impenetrable obscurity of all that might have been but was not.

This certainly is the true character of history and a little reflection will, I confidently believe, convince anyone that it is a far truer representation of the way in which history actually unfolds than the analogue which has so often been suggested in the name of science of a complex mechanism unwinding surely and unalterably toward the end built into it originally. The contrast between these two views of history has been put in a most illuminating way by Oscar Handlin in his book, *Chance or Destiny: Turning Points in American History*.[1] The central part

[1] Little, Brown & Co., 1955

of the book is taken up with recounting in a thoroughly delight-ful way the stories of eight selected crucial events which have constituted turning points in our history. The stories are intro-duced in a Prologue which defines the problem which they raise in the following way:

> "Pondering the degree to which accident overturned the schemes of wise men, Prince Bismarck once concluded that there was a special providence for drunkards, fools, and the United States. And indeed from the point of view of the experienced statesman or the professional soldier there was much to be said for the argument that America had survived and grown strong by a miraculous streak of luck that, at one turning point after another, directed fortune its way. But that raises a serious question as to the nature of such turning points and their place in history. That is the problem to which the stories point."

After recounting the stories, Handlin comments on their im-plications in the following sequence of concise and cogent prop-ositions whose relevance to the problem of the nature of history as we have been viewing it is evident.

> "The denial that chance played a role in history was an act of self-assurance. In the years after 1700, men who leaped eagerly at the future wished, in looking backward, to see the certain evidence of the progress with no hint of luck about it.
>
> "To limit the accidental to a unique event was also a whistling in the dark. It was a way of reaffirming that the past was regular and predictable—except for the one turning point.
>
> "In either form the unwillingness to recognize the effects of chance was a concealment of the truth.
>
> "Is it truer to speak of just eight turning points in American history?
>
> "No! Not if to do so implies that all that transpired between

each of them was orderly and inevitable by the operation of some regularity or law.

"For the turning points are made of such stuff as these: of a shifting wind and a courtier's shyness, of a woman's greed and an old man's hatred, of a metal's failure and a soldier's blunder. Unplanned encounters enter into the shaping of events and so too thoughtless words, the shape of a young girl's face, and the quirks of character of politicians. These are the ingredients that determine the zigzags of history; and the historian can begin to understand its course only when he perceives that it is a line made up of a succession of points, with every point a turning point."

In a lecture on the subject of providence which I gave a short time ago, I used this same quotation to drive home the point about the nature of history which I am making here. After the lecture, in the discussion period which followed, a young graduate student in history asked me a question which he immediately qualified by telling me, "I think you ought to know before you answer that I find Mr. Handlin's view of history repulsive." This is perhaps typical of the reaction which many would have to statements which so emphatically point up the role of chance and accident. Scientific writers speak of it as little as possible when they write on subjects in the historic branches of their sciences. They prefer to dwell on the regular and the dependable whenever it may be found, and to pass over as unobtrusively as possible mention of chance and accident whenever it is necessary to speak of it. But this, as Handlin says, is "a concealment of the truth."

Apart from a knowledge of God as He has revealed Himself first in the life and history of Israel and ultimately in Christ, this truth must always somehow be concealed, for it is intoler-

able. Only the Christian can dare not to make such a concealment, because only for him can "the sundry and manifold
changes of the world" be given a center with respect to which
"his heart may surely there be fixed where true joys are to be
found." It is only Christian meekness which is capable of being
guided in judgment, and it is only Christian contrition and repentance which makes true forgiveness, redemption, and salvation possible. The Christian sees the chances and accidents of
history as the very warp and woof of the fabric of providence
which God is ever weaving. Seen in this way, they can be gladly
and joyously acknowledged and accepted. But apart from this
revelation, chance and accident mean anarchy, sheer meaningless random incoherence, and utter chaos from which the soul
recoils in horror. The truth then must be concealed and some
substitute for Christian providence, or as the Bible would put
it, some idolatry, must be found which will give a source of
hope in spite of chance and accident. But every such hope is
false, a temporary whistling in the dark, a concealment of the
truth. These modern substitutes for divine providence which the
contemporary secular world has adopted for its own peculiar
idolatry will be considered in detail later.

The role of chance and accident in history

The essential and necessary bearing which chance and accident in the shaping of events has on the validity of the Christian
idea of providence can be seen by considering three primary
views of the theme of history which are summed up in the question: Is history the work of God, or of man, or of nature? The
Christian view of divine providence asserts the first about history,
that it unfolds, in the words of the Epistle to the Ephesians, "ac-

cording to the purpose of him who accomplishes all things according to the counsel of his will." The several secular alternatives to providence mentioned above assert the second alternative, believing that history can be made to unfold in accordance with the designs and purposes of mankind provided only that men will place their trust and confidence in the new powers for mastery which science has placed in their hands. The last view is asserted by naturalism, economic determinism, the dialectical materialism of the Marxists, and other forms which make history unfold according to the working of impersonal universal laws within nature herself.

Now the conclusion to which we have been led by the fairly intensive analysis of the nature of scientific knowledge which has been carried out in these pages has shown rather conclusively that neither of the latter two alternatives can account for a theme in history. A history governed by the laws of nature or by the laws of human behavior or by both together cannot be a uniquely determined thing. It is rather a maze, a fabric of turning points, open at every step to new choices and new directions. Yet the path which history takes through this maze produces a story of remarkable yet not fully discernible coherence, a drama which, although its plot remains hidden and secret, moves forward nevertheless with great power and a sense of direction. To this drama the Judeo-Christian tradition gives the name of providence. In the capacity of history to steer a purposeful and meaningful course through the shoals of chance and accident, those who have participated in history as members of this tradition have seen the hand of God in events.

This line of thought can be fruitfully turned around and pursued in the reverse direction. Let us start with the Biblical idea of providence in all its fullness and inquire what kind of a world we must have and what conditions must be satisfied by its history in order to make this idea valid. When the question is put in this way, we see immediately that the first and most important requirement is that it must be a world which is so constituted that its history has at every moment many possibilities open to it. Only in such a world could the course of events be continuously responsive to the will of its Creator. Indeed it was just the narrowing down of opportunities for God's action in history which science seemed to require that led to the tensions which we described in the first chapter. A world in which the laws of nature uniquely determine the history of nature is a closed and self-contained world. Only by radical intervention can its Creator act in any way in its history. The exercise of providence by intervention in this way is, however, quite unlike the Biblical understanding of providence. This understanding can be valid and real only in a world whose history is open, and remains open even when man makes his best efforts to close it upon a course of his own design. It is just such a history which the role of chance and accident in the shaping of events insures.

There are two primary sources of indeterminacy in history. One of these is chance. When we speak of chance as a factor in history, we have in mind the existence, as a typical feature of natural processes, of alternative responses to a given set of causative influences for which the laws of nature specify only the relative probabilities. Insofar as alternatives are typical of all natural processes, chance becomes a universal ingredient of history. But there is another equally important source of indeterminism in history. This is accident. The accidental as used here in connection with the nature of history refers to situations in which two or more chains of events which have no causal connection with each other coincide in such a way as to decide the course of events. The accidental does not depend on the presence of choice and alternative in natural phenomena. Two chains of events could each be rigorously determined within themselves and yet be such that their accidental convergence would decisively modify the course of history. Several crucial military victories have been due to the unexpected arrival of a storm at just the right moment. Yet the meteorological conditions which brought about the storm and the military strategy which led up to the battle are in no way related. Accident and chance are similar in their effects on history, but they are nevertheless independent and quite separate factors. The accidental would be operative even if the chance selection of alternatives were not a factor, as the above example shows. Yet both are in fact operative in history as we know it.

The role of the dependable and reliable in history

In attempting to make clear the openness of history as a necessary condition for the validity of the Judeo-Christian idea of providence, there is danger of failing to do justice to the extent to which the coherent and dependable are present in history. Much of the mystery and strangeness of history arises from the intimate and often paradoxical manner in which chance and accident are combined with coherence and dependability within it. It will be well therefore to pause here and take note of the predictable and reliable in history.

One form of dependability in history which is a basic factor for all life on earth is the regularity of the rising and setting of the sun and the cycles of the seasons. Night and day in their regular alternations represent completely reliable and dependable elements of our existence in time. So, too, with the phases of the moon which have led to the division of our year into months and the somewhat less precise but equally dependable succession of the seasons through the course of a year. Here we have an example of a primary ingredient of history which arises out of a physical situation which remains, as we have already seen, the most important and accurate example of the determinism of classical mechanics. There are, as has been noted before, some cases of natural phenomena in which the typical situation of alternatives governed by probabilities goes over into the special case of a single alternative in which only one thing can happen. As explained before, this arises when the laws of nature prescribe essentially zero probabilities for all alternative modes of behavior other than the single possibility. The solar system is one of these special cases and the phenomena associated with it share in consequence the reliability associated with its rigorously determined motions.

Reliability and coherence of a different sort arise from phenomena involving several alternatives in which large numbers of repeated instances can be counted upon to convert probabilities into near certainties. This form of coherence in nature is much more widespread than the other. An important example is the constancy and dependability of the radiation received from the sun. The source of this radiation resides in thermonuclear reactions, of essentially the same character as those involved in the so-called hydrogen bomb, which go on in the central core of the sun. Each of the individual nuclear reactions involved in this process depend on the selection of a highly improbable alternative by individual nuclear particles involved in random collisions with each other. Yet such really enormous numbers of such collisions occur in a short time interval like a second that even the extremely small probabilities involved become practical certainties. As a result the amount of energy released can be counted upon with great accuracy to be the same for every time interval of a second's duration year in and year out. Much in our given historic situation depends on the constancy of this radiation. Among the many elements which require it may be cited the mean temperature of the earth's surface, the weather, photosynthesis in plants, and protective measures against sunburn.

Other examples of coherence and dependability in nature which are due to this same source are the freezing of water at 32° F; the burning of wood, coal, and other fuels; the strength of a steel girder; or the regular beating of our hearts or expansion and contraction of our lungs in breathing. Our lives depend on the reliability of great numbers of such processes. The long history of the universe is filled with them and indeed without the coherence and dependability which they provide we would not be able to write its history at all. They constitute a sure foundation on which history can build and weave a coherent and uniform fabric on which the design of history can be embroidered. In giving so much emphasis to the role of chance and accident in history in order to make manifest the role of providence, we must not lose sight of the impressive degree to which coherence and dependability are found in it, or even indeed the extent to which providence itself relies upon this aspect.

Even in the realm of individual and social human behavior

there is a considerable amount of coherence and dependability of this type as the successful instances of psychology and sociology have shown. Military action and strategy depend on the reliability of human behavior under given circumstances. Conditioning and learning processes can be applied in ways which are becoming more and more reliable to increase the probability of a desired mode of behavior and correspondingly decrease the probabilities of all its undesirable alternatives. The stability, coherence, and effectiveness of organizations, institutions, and corporations depend on the reliability of human behavior, and there is such a thing as a true science of management which can be applied toward the achievement of such dependability. So, too, government and politics involve much that is coherent and reliable, and political science is in consequence a bona fide and valuable discipline.

In this area of human behavior, however, we already see clearly the intermingling of chance and accident with the coherent and reliable which is so characteristic of the historic process. Here the numbers involved are much smaller and the repetitions of the same process much less frequent than in the physical, chemical, and physiological processes which we used earlier as examples. As a result the degree of certainty that the probabilities will be actualized is much less, and the relative importance of isolated instances of the improbable correspondingly greater. The military commander, the executive, or the statesman can never be sure that a mode of behavior radically different from that on which he based his plans will not occur.

Science as it endeavors to gain understanding of the world selects phenomena for study which are capable of frequent repetition under controlled conditions. By analyzing its results statistically it emerges with well determined values for the probabilities of occurrence of the several available alternatives. With these in hand it rests its hope on a confidence that the most probable can be counted upon to happen. History on the other hand controls no conditions and often does not allow repetitions of phenomena. It has a way of selecting the most improbable alternatives and, by combining them judiciously with the most unexpected accidents, of building with them major consequences which in the words of the Magnificat "scatter the proud in the imagination of their hearts." Thus history, providence, and destiny, which are three of a kind, rest their hope, contrary to science, on a confidence that the most improbable can be counted upon to happen. And therein lies one of the sources of the latent hostility between science and providence out of which has risen in part some of the tension which we are hoping to elucidate. This hostility is none other than an age-old hostility in a new guise; one which has always arisen between human pride and divine judgment, between man's will and God's will.

Providence not a new force as in vitalism

When we tie the Biblical idea of providence as closely as we have to the role of chance and accident in history, there is danger of a misunderstanding based on the application of a very common error concerning the nature of providence. This error consists in regarding providence as an added non-physical force in nature whose operation produces discernible and verifiable empirical consequences by means of which it can be objectively established. We Christians are quite prone to fall into this error and to seem to argue with the secular world that evidence for

God's providential guidance and purpose in events is as clear and incontrovertible as the empirical evidence which can be had for the effect of a natural force like an electric field on the same events. This is frequently implied in various forms of the teleological argument for the existence of God. In other forms it appears as what is called vitalism in biology and spiritualism in psychology. Whatever its form, it seeks to establish the fact of providence as an objectively discernible feature of the world on a comparable basis with the laws of nature.

Providence, however, is not simply an additional force which supplements the forces within nature herself. Vitalism and spiritualism are as alien to the Biblical understanding of providence as they are to the spirit of science. From the side of science the testimony is overwhelming that scientific investigation by itself does not lead to any empirical evidence at all for such extranatural forces entering into and controlling phenomena. All that science arrives at in this direction is the detection of chance and probability. In the nature of things it cannot go farther. When we have arrived at the probabilities governing an elementary process and established them as true probabilities following the laws of chance processes, then science has nothing more it can say about the process. When science arrives at chance and accident in history, no amount of ingenuity, new experimentation, or fresh techniques can convert it into anything other than chance and accident. This is a real stopping point so long as we are limited to the detached objective attitude toward events which is essential to science.

Pierre Lecomte du Noüy in his book, *Human Destiny*,[2] tries

[2] du Noüy, Pierre Lecomte, *Human Destiny*, Longmans Green & Co., Inc., New York, 1947.

to argue otherwise. But his arguments make improper use of scientific results, and they treat chance and probability in a wholly fallacious way. His objective is to penetrate scientifically the barrier of chance and accident and so demonstrate by purely empirical-rational means that God's active providence in the evolutionary process is as objectively essential to an understanding of it as any of its empirically ascertainable constituents, such as genes, gene mutations, or the process of natural selection. If, however, it were possible to carry through successfully such a program, then it would be possible to arrive at the Christian perception and understanding of providence quite independently of God's historic revelation of Himself to which the Bible bears witness. To paraphrase St. Paul in a different context, it would then be true that "Christ died for nothing." Quite a number of Christians welcomed Lecomte du Noüy's book when it appeared, chiefly because it was a relief to see a contemporary book in scientific terms which frankly acknowledged the reality of God and of His continuing activity in the world. Yet such a book does the cause of Christian apologetics no good both because, on the one hand, it explicitly claims to be able to arrive at central Christian affirmations about God entirely independently of His historic revelation of Himself in Christ, and, on the other hand, because it completely fails to convince anyone in the scientific community who is not already convinced by a totally different route.

But if it is true that we cannot penetrate behind chance and accident in history to establish objectively God's purposive activity in the shaping of events, it is equally true that we cannot penetrate the same curtain to satisfy ourselves that such activity is not present. This, however, is a frequent error of those in the secular camp. The evolutionist, G. G. Simpson, in his book, *The Meaning of Evolution*, states the problem we are concerned with here in the following terms:

> "In attempting to interpret this history (i.e., the history of life on earth) the major problem, both philosophical and scientific, is to decide whether it has taken place under the action of universal and natural principles, and so is materialistic; whether it has involved principles new in and peculiar to life, making it vitalistic; and whether, in either case, it does or does not represent the working out of some supernal purpose, involving an over-all plan and progressing toward a goal, the finalistic interpretation."[3]

At this point as he has done on many other occasions throughout his book, Simpson proceeds to reiterate the adequacy of natural, non-vitalistic processes for understanding the course of evolution and to reject vitalism both as unnecessary and as lacking any basis in the evidence. In this last contention, I find myself in full agreement with him. On the question of purpose, however, he first points out that a careful and objective examination of the facts of the history of life as biological evolution presents them fails to reveal what the purpose of the story is. In this conclusion any historian would agree with him, pointing out that it is equally true of any history. Instead of a defined purpose which emerges clearly and evidently from the trend of the story itself, he finds, most significantly from the standpoint of our present discussion, only chance and accident! As he says, "Solutions are not achieved in the way theoretically best but on the basis of what happens to be available, apparently by

[3] Simpson, George Gaylord, *The Meaning of Evolution,* Yale University Press, 1949, p. 342.

chance."[4] And again, "Although many details remain to be worked out, it is already evident that all the objective phenomena of the history of life can be explained . . . on the basis of differential reproduction in populations . . . and of the mainly random interplay of the known processes of heredity."[5]

Having thus found that the plan of history cannot be discerned from the facts of history and that objective evidence of the course of events leads us to acknowledge only accident (what happened to be available) and chance (the random interplay of genetic factors), he leaps on this basis to a conclusion which he states positively, dogmatically, and without reservation:

> "Man is the result of a purposeless and materialistic process that did not have him in mind. He was not planned."[6]
>
> "Discovery that the universe apart from man or before his coming lacks and lacked any purpose or plan has the inevitable corollary that the workings of the universe cannot provide any automatic, universal, eternal, or absolute ethical criteria of right and wrong."[7]

It should be patently evident, even to Mr. Simpson, that these are things he cannot possibly know with anything like the assurance he pretends. They certainly do not follow from any of the objective evidence in his book, which, as he is careful to point out wherever he presents it, only leads to chance and accident. But neither purpose nor purposelessness can be deduced from them. To attempt either is, as Mr. Handlin says in a passage previously quoted, "a whistling in the dark" and "a concealment of the truth." When we look at the story of America as Mr.

[4] *Ibid.*, p. 342
[5] *Ibid.*, p. 343
[6] *Ibid.*, p. 344
[7] *Ibid.*, p. 345

Handlin depicts it and contemplate "the miraculous streak of luck that, at one turning point after another, directed fortune its way," who would want to say that this is proof positive that America has no destiny? The story of the history of life over the last billion years on this planet as Simpson tells it is also one which, considering the random chances and improbable associations which are its primary objective ingredients, can also only seem like a miraculous streak of luck which at one turning point after another carried it forward from the first protogenes to the production of man. Who can say when confronted with this story whether or not it implies that creation too has no destiny?

There is no way in which one can use the discovery of chance and accident in history to prove anything about the purpose of history. All it can possibly show is that history is open and pregnant with many possibilities. We see clearly that history objectively considered did not have to be the way it was. Innumerable other histories involving very different courses of events were just as possible and could just as well have happened as the history which did in fact occur. Objectively considered, it is a pure happenstance that the world has the history it does have and not any one of the others it could equally well have had. It should be quite clear that chance and accident could not possibly establish anything beyond this and still really remain chance and accident. It is just as fallacious to try to wring from them a proof of purposelessness as it is to try to use them to establish objectively the Christian idea of providence.

The Christian idea of providence

The Christian idea of providence is an insight into a range of reality which is inaccessible to any detached, uninvolved, strictly objective way of apprehending the world. The reality and the truth which it comprehends is even more vividly real than is the level of reality accessible through science, but the validity of the access to reality which Christianity provides does not rest on the same basis as the validity of scientific knowledge. There is, however, one way in which the validity of the two types of knowledge share a common base. They are both knowledge gained, shared, and understood in community. In the case of science it is the members of the several professional scientific communities who possess and fully share with each other the knowledge of their science. Efforts at popularization of such knowledge for the benefit of those outside the community, i.e., for non-scientists, are notoriously inadequate. Most importantly, they fail to convey any adequate sense of the basis of the validity of the knowledge being communicated. My discourse in the previous chapter on classical and quantum mechanics may or may not have been intelligible or interesting to my readers, but one thing it positively could not do was to convey to them a sense of the validity of its conclusions with anything like the strength, scope, and convincing power which physicists enjoy in their discussions of the same topics. In like manner, Simpson's book from which we have just quoted contains an excellent presentation of the fascinating story of evolution for the general reader, but his sense of frustration in trying to convey a recognition of the validity of the underlying processes of genetic change and natural selection, which is anything like as potent and deep and vivid as that which geneticists enjoy naturally, is very evident throughout.

So, too, is Christian knowledge even more a knowledge shared in community; the community of the faithful in Christ

Jesus which is the Holy Catholic Church. Here, too, efforts to popularize this knowledge for the pagan world have always been unsatisfactory and there is no way in which they can convey the sense of the validity, reality, and unique access to the living truth which members of the community enjoy naturally. Yet the knowledge here differs in kind from objective scientific knowledge. This difference arises from the fact that it is given or revealed knowledge in contrast to earned or discovered knowledge. This arises from the nature of the community, the Church, within which it has been received, has been and is now shared, and out of which witness to it is borne. For the community in question is a covenant community which, first as Israel under the old covenant, and then as the Church under the new, has lived its whole history in an intimate relationship and bond with Almighty God. The fruit of this relationship is a knowledge of the living personal God which is inaccessible and even unthinkable apart from the relationship, just as the knowledge which husband and wife have of each other and reveal to each other is inaccessible and unthinkable outside the marriage bond. Living the life of the community in worship and sacrament, in repentance and forgiveness, and sharing fully in the grace which abounds within it, the fullness of its heritage, and the wealth of its tradition and historic witness, the Christian comes to share this deep personal and living knowledge of our Lord, and to know God through "the Word made flesh and dwelling among us so that we beheld His glory."

The God, who has thus revealed Himself to those who within this holy community have become members of the household of God, has made Himself known primarily as the God who acts in human life and human history. In every situation and in every

event throughout the whole of His creation, animate and inanimate alike, He acts in might, in power, and in mercy. He
chastens in judgment and heals in redemption. As history unfolds, it proceeds in accordance with the mysterious purpose of
His will. Apart from His living presence and power, history
would disintegrate into sheer chaos, striving in its openness of
alternative like the proverbial horseman to dash off in every
direction at once. This is the Christian idea of providence, and
it is given not through any dispassionate analysis of external
phenomena, not through any discovered vitalism or spiritualism
or other supernatural principle pervading nature, but by revelation to His people, through their historic experience within the
covenant relationship, by Almighty God Himself.

We must explore in detail in the next chapter the concrete
character of the knowledge of providence thus revealed. Here,
however, we shall confine ourselves to contrasting those who
enjoy this added gift of insight into the source of the living,
dynamic reality of life, with those whose apprehension of the
world is imprisoned by the secular, and who therefore can only
see reality through the limited route of science. Science, for
all its wonderful achievements, can of itself see nothing of God,
since it is constrained to deal only with that which is objective
and set over against us as observing subjects, and with respect
to which, therefore, we cannot become involved. When the
Christian views history through the eyes of his secular colleagues
and sees with them its innumerable alternatives and openness,
he senses immediately that this is exactly the character which
history, objectively considered, must have in order to be able
to be the same as that which has been revealed to him as the
history of which Christ is Lord. The elementary barrier of chance

and accident against which objective knowledge halts is just what is required to make this so. It is what in his own experience of the mystery of grace, threading through the chances and accidents of his own life, he has come to recognize as the very means which God employs to prevent us from searching out the mystery of His will and of thereby succumbing to the danger which our sinful nature makes inevitable—of using our knowledge of Him to achieve the purposes of our own wills. Indeed, what is it other than the chance happening and the accidental development which foils the plans which men in their pride make for themselves? What else prevents man from making himself the captain of his soul and the master of his fate? So the Christian does not resent or rebel against the barrier of chance and accident, but welcomes it gladly for what it is, humbling himself before it instead of vainly combatting it, because he knows that through it the lovely mystery of grace comes to him in his own life.

Secular man, on the other hand, cannot rest content with this barrier. Simply to leave history open and indeterminate, making what has happened in the past and what can be planned for in the future simply quixotic and whimsical, like the spin of a roulette wheel, is intolerable. He pins his hopes on science's ability to probe somehow and sometime behind chance and accident, uncover their roots, and eliminate the uncomfortable openness and indeterminacy which they introduce into history. But as we have seen, chance appears to be essential to scientific knowledge, not because of any merely temporary inadequacy of science, but because the world which science investigates is made in a certain way. If the laws built into the natural world really do permit through chance and accident many alternative courses for its history, as we Christians are convinced that they must, then secular man cannot by the very nature of things find anything within nature herself capable of removing this indeterminacy. Once he comes to see this clearly, perhaps he will be willing to come with us, as we so earnestly wish that he would. If he will but sample the rich heritage which we share and by which we live, he will have his eyes opened to a new vista of reality out of which profound meaning, a revived sense of destiny, and a living purpose will emerge, as with a developing photograph, out of the blankness and meaninglessness which the intellectual bondage to an exclusive dependence on scientific knowledge of nature inevitably produces. This is our offer to him, and we hold the invitation ever open. He will be welcome and received with joy when he comes.

4

CHANCE, TIME, AND MIRACLE

In the preceding chapter we referred to chance and accident
as an elementary barrier behind which we should never be
able to penetrate. We shall devote ourselves in this chapter to an
analysis of this statement. It is vital to the integrity of our central
thesis concerning the relationship between the Christian idea of
providence, and the presence of chance and accident in events to
understand just why and how this barrier cannot be penetrated.

Chance in individual events

Chance and probability are peculiar and rather elusive notions
at the outset. Unlike all other elements which enter into a
scientific description of phenomena, they do not apply to any

concrete happening. Yet at the same time we must, if they are to have any value at all, use them as though they did apply to individual events. This circumstance gives to the language of probability a baffling character which can be the occasion for numerous misconceptions and inadvertently erroneous usages.

I can easily calculate that the chance of a four spot coming up on the cast of a perfect die is one-sixth. If now I cast the die and a four spot does turn up, there is no operation whatever which I can perform with respect to that throw which will prove that the probability actually realized in that throw was one-sixth. The only proof of this sort which I can undertake would apply not to this particular throw but to a very large number of re-peated throws in which I might indeed satisfy myself that the four spot does come up one-sixth of the time. In most scientific applications of probability theory this difficulty is not crucial either because it does not matter what comes up in a single throw or because all that is being studied anyhow is the pattern formed by a large number of repeated throws. But it becomes a very different matter when, say, a man's life depends on a four turn-ing up, and a four does turn up. It is doubtful whether, in re-flecting on this event thereafter, he could ever be satisfied by the simple assertion that the chance of his living then was exactly one-sixth. Would he not always wonder why it was that, when a four spot was just what was needed, it was a four spot which turned up?

It is only when we are dealing with large numbers of repeated instances at a given time that probabilities are actualized in events. In the field of natural phenomena this is, as we have seen, the basis on which science rests. In the field of affairs it is the basis for all forms of insurance underwriting, the stock exchange, and the operation of gambling establishments. History, on the other hand, involves in its most significant and determining aspects only non-repetitive events. The crucial events of history, the turning points if you wish, are singular, and the assignment of probabilities to them is either fruitless or misleading. A life insurance company could specify fairly accurately the probability of the death during the coming year of any one of the present heads of state of the nations of the world. The effect on world history of the actual death of one of them would, however, be in no way measured by the probability of its occurrence. Again, geneticists may be able to state accurately the probability of some of the mutations which have been crucial in setting the course of the evolutionary process. The knowledge of such probabilities is, however, of little assistance to the paleontologist who seeks to understand the course which was actually taken.

There is a stark and sturdy impregnability about events which constitutes their singularity. It is indeed just this impregnability which gives an elemental character to the barrier which chance and accident throw up in the path of a purely scientific understanding of history. The difficulty with the attempt to understand history in scientific terms is that the role of any given event in shaping history is generally entirely unrelated to the manner in which that same event fits into the probability pattern formed by the class of all such events when repeated a large number of times under the same conditions. The determination of the probability of throwing a four spot with a given die is a proper subject for scientific investigation. It cannot, however, illuminate in any way the mystery for the man whose life was saved because in a single throw a four spot actually did turn up.

CHANCE AND PROVIDENCE

Chance cannot be a cause

An error which frequently creeps into discussions of historical events in terms of scientific results is that of treating chance as being in itself a causative agent. In this use of the term it is said of an event that it "was due to chance" or of another that it "was not due to chance" as though chance itself could be the reason behind the event. Numerous scientific people desiring to correct what are believed to be popular misconceptions of religious origin about the cause of evolution or the origin of life have argued against the reality of divine providence on the basis of explaining the course of events as the result of chance. By describing steps in the process in terms of known physical, chemical, or biological processes whose probabilities could in principle be determined by experiment in the laboratory today, they imply that the cause of such steps has been identified as chance. Since, the argument runs, the process is now seen to be the result of chance, the older ideas of divine involvement in creation no longer hold. On the other side of such arguments the same error is made by those, such as Lecomte du Noüy to whom reference has already been made, who strive to show that the process cannot be explained by chance. Both modes of argument are equally fallacious because chance as such simply cannot be the cause or reason for anything happening.

It is very important to understand this point clearly since it is the basis of so much widespread misunderstanding. Actually the attribution of chance to events is just the opposite of the assertion of their cause. This point has been made very forcefully by P. W. Bridgman in a recent issue of *Science:*[1]

[1] "Probability, Logic and ESP," in *Science,* vol. 123, p. 16, January 6, 1956.

"If we are prodded to tell exactly what we mean when we say 'this past event was chance', we admit that there is no property inherent in the event by which we can verify that it actually was chance, and we seek for the meaning elsewhere.

"We may seek the meaning of 'was chance' in what we do about it. Now the paradoxical thing is that when we say 'was chance', we do nothing about it—we have come to the end. The reason we have come to the end is that consistency with our position forbids that we attempt to go further. If we went ahead and sought for an explanation or any sort of rational involvement, we would be stultifying our conclusion that the event was chance. As long as we remain consistent and do nothing, we are safe. . . . In fact, the operational meaning of 'this *was* chance' involves our resolution to handle the situation just by doing nothing."

The assertion of chance is the dead end in the path of causal explanation. The very idea of probability requires valid alternatives of response to a given cause or set of causes. Insofar as these alternatives are real, the question as to why a particular one was selected in a particular instance must not be posed. For if it is answerable in terms of natural causes, even in principle, then there would not be a probability for the event in question but instead certainty. Probability applies to indeterminate events. If in the course of further investigation the indeterminacies are removed by showing the several alternatives to be really different situations in which different sets of causes are operative, the description of the several phenomena in terms of chance and probability is immediately dropped. Thereafter one speaks simply of what must happen. But so long as we speak of chance at all, we have, as Bridgman says, "come to the end." The consistency of our position demands that we do nothing further toward causal explanation.

Relationship between chance and providence

These considerations help to clarify the intimate relationship between chance as it is involved in a scientific description of events and providence as it is known in the Biblical sense. Science deals with repeatable events for which the laws of nature determine probabilities of occurrence. Providence in the Biblical sense deals with isolated singular events apprehended in a given historical context as responsive to God's will. One and the same event can equally well be regarded as under the full sway of all laws of nature and natural causality and at the same time under the full sway of the divine will. The reason is that the laws of nature prescribe only the chance or probability of the event under the given set of circumstances in which it occurred. But a knowledge of this probability in no way affects the providential character of the event, which depends only on the circumstance that that particular possibility was the one which actually did occur in the historical sequence of which it was a part. Science deals with a single happening only in terms of the way it falls into the pattern of repeatable events which can happen in a given set of circumstances. Providence, however, ignores all else which might have happened but didn't, and focuses its attention on the one thing which did happen in a given setting in history. The context of science is the laboratory where things happen over and over under the same controlled conditions. The context of providence is history which happens only once. What is labeled chance in one context can without contradiction manifest the will of God acting in judgment or in redemption in the other. It is in this way that a world ruled by God and responsive to His will can be at the same time a world capable of scientific description in terms of natural law and natural causality.

A common objection which is often raised against the idea of providence is that it implies an upsetting or distortion by God of the "natural" probability pattern of events in order to achieve His purposes. Such an objection arises out of the erroneous application to providence of the mode of operation of natural causes. In a scientific description of phenomena, we are accustomed to thinking of the operation of natural causes in terms of the changed pattern of probabilities which they produce. Perturbing forces in quantum mechanics change the probabilities of occupancy of the available quantum states in proportion to the strength and duration of the perturbations. In genetics, changes in temperature, chemical environment, and radiation intensity produce corresponding changes in the rates with which various mutations occur. Progress in medicine and public health are reflected in corresponding changes in the probability of death as reflected in the life insurance mortality tables. With this background of experience in science it is natural to carry over the same mode of thought into considerations of the divine activity. This is particularly true for those who think of God as some sort of extra-natural spiritual force akin to an electromagnetic field. Providence in such a mode of thought would operate by applying suitable pressures in the form of spiritual forces to history in such a way as to make some alternatives more probable and others less. Such a mode of operation of the divine will would of course imply a modification of the "natural" probability patterns of events through divine intervention. It is evidently some such analogy between divine and natural causation which people have in mind when they object that providence must imply that God manipulates probabilities.

But any such notion of the divine activity in history is completely non-Biblical. Providence is made manifest in single events, not in multiple tries to which probabilities can be assigned. Consider any happening of which it might be asserted that it occurred because God willed that it should. What bearing does such an assertion have upon the probability of the happening in the context of the natural conditions and causes surrounding it? The answer is clearly, none at all. With sufficient effort we could perhaps duplicate the total situation of the happening with these same conditions and causes and so by repeating it over and over determine what the probability of the particular happening was. But there is clearly no way in which we could apply our result to the historical occurrence about which the assertion of providential character had been made. Whether it was probable or improbable, the fact remains that it did happen. That is the stubborn fact about events in history which no amount of repetition under controlled conditions can soften. Moreover, the providential character of the event is completely unaffected by subsequent scientific studies of the same class of events which may be carried out. It is clearly of the essence of the idea of providence that there be no compulsion on the will of God to act in the same way on subsequent repetitions of the event as He did act when it occurred in its historical context. It lies at the heart of the Biblical idea of providence that there be no method of verifying by means of controlled tests or experiments whether or not a particular event in the past occurred because God willed that that particular alternative should be selected on that particular occasion.

These considerations make it clear that the one characteristic of the scientific description of the world which we require in order to have the kind of world in which the Biblical view can be true is the description of phenomena in terms of chance and probability. Thus the Christian should never fear the assertion of chance by his secular colleagues but rather welcome it enthusiastically. Those secular writers who feel that they have demolished the Biblical view of creation and evolution as soon as they have established the statistical character of the phenomena involved, have unwittingly done the one thing necessary to sustain that view. Often they seek to clinch their case by asserting that the course of events was the consequence of "mere chance." But the use of the adjective "mere" describes only the prejudices and bias of the author. Neither science nor mathematics knows a special kind of chance which can be so qualified. They know only the simple unqualified objective fact of chance and probability. Those Christian writers who strive so laboriously to prove that the events of history could not have been the result of chance only play into the hands of their secular opponents. To Einstein's famous question expressing his abhorrence of quantum mechanics, "Does God throw dice?" the Judeo-Christian answer is not, as so many have wrongly supposed, a denial, but a very positive affirmative. For only in a world in which the laws of nature govern events in accordance with the casting of dice can the Biblical view of a world whose history is responsive to God's will prevail.

Scientific time

Another way to approach the intimate connection between chance and providence is through a consideration of their place

97

in time. For this purpose a distinction must be made between two kinds of time which may be called for convenience *scientific time* and *historical time*. Time as we know it and experience it is both of these kinds of time together, yet they are very different in character. Scientific time is, as the adjective implies, the kind of time employed in science while historical time is the kind of time used in history. Scientific time is the kind of time measured by a clock. It has extension and can be marked off in seconds, hours, and years. Historical time has no extension and cannot be measured. It can only be lived. It is made up of three domains—past, present, and future—each of which is different and possesses its own distinctive character.

Scientific time has as its most distinguishing characteristic the possibility of representing it by means of a line in space. This is done, for example, whenever we make a graph with time as a coordinate. If we plot the population of a city, the employment of a company, the market value of a stock, or the position of a planet against time, we represent time by a line which is scored off in days, months, or years. A clock converts time into a path in space swept out by the points of the hands as they move over its face. A railroad timetable associates times with positions or stations along a track which is a line in space. In all these cases the time involved is scientific time.

Now it is characteristic of a line in space that every point on it has the same status as every other. There is no special or distinctive point. When one plots something against time on a graph, one must always arbitrarily decide where to set the origin of the time axis. On the graph the axis for time is, of course, a line segment with a beginning and an end. But one can easily think of extending it indefinitely in either direction so that the line extends to infinity each way. In itself it has no beginning, center, or end. The apparent beginning and end of the time axis on our graph were arbitrarily imposed on the line of time by us from the outside to suit our own purposes. So too, a clock must be arbitrarily set to conform with a given present. In itself it has no beginning or end. *83848*

As a result of this property scientific time has no past, present, or future inherent in itself. If the solution of any scientific problem is plotted against time, the point representing the present moment must be marked on it as an arbitrary act imposed upon the solution from other considerations which are not a part of the problem itself. Once this has been done we *interpret* all parts of the graph to the left of this mark as past states of the system which the graph represents and all of it to the right of this mark as future states. The scientific problem, however, makes no such distinction. Past, present, and future do not belong to it or inhere in it as a proper part of the problem. The equations describing the motions of the earth and moon which are used to predict when eclipses of the sun will occur in the future are used in exactly the same way to find out when eclipses occurred in the past. The equations themselves involve time in the same way as space coordinates and all "times" in them are on the same footing. They know of no past, present, or future at all. It is only we, who use the equations of science to interpret phenomena, who impose upon them historical time in order to decide which portions represent what has already happened and so are past, and which portions represent what is to come and so are future. Even in the simple case of a railroad timetable there is no way of telling what portions of it are past and what are future. The traveller at a particular station decides that when he examines the timetable in order to see whether he has missed the train or can look forward to taking it.

Historical time

Unlike scientific time, historical time has as its most distinctive feature a fixed point, the *now,* which is not the least bit arbitrary. This point separates two domains which are essentially different in character, the past and the future. All existence is inexorably imprisoned in the *now,* and it is the most unalterable condition of our existence that there is no escape from it. We may and sometimes do wish that we could escape this present and live in some other period. The comic strip, Alley Oop, speaks to this desire with its "time machine" with which men might at will transport themselves to distant epochs of the past or future. But we all recognize this as pure fantasy. The one thing there is absolutely no escape from is the present moment. The point in time which we are given to live in must be accepted. We along with all else which exists are trapped in it.

Behind this point stretches the domain of the past, the record of all that has already happened, the reservoir of the dead and gone, the accumulation of all that existed or happened in previous "nows." The characteristic of the past is its unalterability. Once a thing has happened it must always forever after be that way. There is no way in which we can get back into the past and alter one jot or tittle of it. The general who lost a crucial battle may agonizingly review it over and over thereafter, re-enacting it in his mind with a different strategy, but it has no effect on the battle as it in fact took place. No amount of longing for what might have been will alter in any way what was. History differs from science primarily in the absolute inability of the historian to experiment with his material. In seeking to understand the course of events in the past, he can never test his hypotheses by seeing how things would have turned out if some other things had been different. There is only one past for the whole universe and insofar as we can discover what it was we must accept it in detail without thought of modification or change.

On the other side of the *now* in historical time lies the domain of the future. This domain is very different in character and structure from the domain of the past. The most distinctive characteristic of the future is the endless variety of its possibilities. The future is pregnant with potentiality. The one thing we know most deeply about it is, as every gambler will testify, that until a thing has actually happened almost anything can happen. In complete contrast to the past where all is unalterable and irrevocable, the domain of the future is open and alterable. In it everything is possible and nothing is absolutely required. Even in those aspects of the world to which classical mechanics continues to be most rigorously applicable we cannot bring ourselves to assert an absolute requirement on the future. Who, for example, could bring himself to say that tomorrow morning at the end of this coming night the sun is absolutely certain to rise? Surely a cosmic catastrophe would be required to prevent its doing so. But who would be willing to assert that it is really impossible for such a catastrophe to occur between now and tomorrow morning? Everything in the future is governed by probability, not necessity.

Historical time is the time in which we live our lives. It is only in the present that life is lived, decisions taken, and commitments made. Our past is the ordered array of the events which took place in all earlier nows. But it does not exist as we now exist. It resides only in memory and can only be recalled, never actualized. We cannot get to it and undo it, for it is dead and gone. Our future on the other hand lies ahead of us, pregnant with possibilities. It does not exist as we now exist but resides only in anticipation. The future keeps coming at us with its open alternatives among which we must, whether we will or no, select one and forever reject all the others. We cannot slow it down, put it off, or avoid it in any way. It will not wait for us but moves steadily, inexorably upon us. The alternatives it presents must be chosen. The primary requirement of historical time is that only one of the possible alternatives coming at you from the future can be actualized in the present where it will flow into the past and remain forever after unalterable. You may sometimes have "another chance" and be able to make a different choice in some later present, but this can in no way change the choice you did in fact make in the first instance. This is the quality of historical time as it is experienced by those who live in it. It is a very different thing from scientific time, although that too is a real form of time. Act and deed, acceptance and rejection, choice and decision, commitment and vow, adventure and courage are all words which belong to historical time, but have no meaning in scientific time.

Probability brings historical time into science

The most thoroughgoing application of scientific time to the phenomenal world is that which is made in the special and general theories of relativity of Albert Einstein. Here the characteristic of scientific time which allows it to be represented as a line in space becomes actualized by the conversion of time into a true space-like dimension possessing all the geometrical properties of space itself. This is possible because of the status of the velocity of light as a fixed universal constant of nature having the same value for all observers regardless of their state of motion with respect to a source of light. Because of this property, times can be converted to distances in a uniform manner simply by multiplying them by this constant velocity. As a result time in relativity theory becomes simply a fourth space-like dimension which like any line in space can be explored at will from one end to the other. A graph of any element in nature—of an electron, a bird, or the earth—can be drawn in this four dimensional space-time to represent not only all positions occupied in space by the object, but its whole past and future as well, in a single completed entity called in the theory a "world-line." From the standpoint of relativity theory the present is merely an accidental point on the time axis like the location of Boston, Washington, or Miami on federal highway No. 1. Events in this theory cannot be said to "happen"; they simply "take place." Properly speaking, they can only be thought of as being recorded, observed, or awaited, depending on whether they are past, present, or future. A world-line is like a railroad timetable which consolidates information about where a train was, is, and will be into a single complete entity.

Such a thoroughgoing application of scientific time eliminates completely the centrality and givenness of the present moment and the radical distinction between past and future which constitute the essential realities of historical time. In the world described by relativity theory life in time is like the slow rolling up of a shade to reveal an already completed picture behind it.

The past is merely that portion of the picture already uncovered, and the future the remaining portion not yet revealed. There is no qualitative difference between them since they are both portions of the same picture. The lower edge of the curtain constitutes the present where, in our ignorance, we think that life is being lived, events really happening, chances taken, decisions made, responsibility exercised, and success or failure decided. But really it is nothing more than the edge of the curtain and we, together with all other creatures of history, no more than spectators of the moving edge of time waiting to see each new segment of the picture as it is uncovered.

Perhaps the most significant aspect for science as a whole of the discovery of the uncertainty principle in physics can be stated in terms of these two kinds of time. For one way of stating what the uncertainty principle did to mechanics is to say that it introduced for the first time in an unavoidable way historical time into a description of reality which prior to then had been exclusively concerned with scientific time. Classical physics had made much use of probabilities and statistical methods in general, but it did so only as a practical way of simplifying otherwise very complex problems. Chance and probability entered only as devices to circumvent the necessity of inquiring into details which were irrelevant to the primary concern. It was always possible to suppose that the statistical character of macroscopic processes would, on minute examination of each individual step, prove to be fully determined by the laws of mechanics. But in quantum mechanics the uncertainty principle permits no such circumventing of the implications of statistical behavior and probability. Chance and probabilty in modern physics are, as we have seen, real and essential elements of the world which it describes. They apply in a universal way to the most elementary and simplest components of the world.

By introducing alternative modes of response to the same set of causes, with the mode selected in individual instances a matter of chance measured by a probability, the uncertainty principle has made historical time an essential component of science. In order even to define probability it is essential to distinguish a *now* in which a selection among alternatives is made, bounded by a *future* with all alternatives potential in it, and a *past* in which one alternative must be selected and all the others rejected. This, however, is the essence of historical time. Wherever they occur in science, chance and probability force upon it the reality of historical time. Yet historical time is really unnatural and alien to science. It is scientific time which is exclusively employed in all fields of science wherever and whenever possible. It is only through chance and probability, and then only when there is no way to avoid recognizing them as real and essential elements of phenomena, that historical time enters science at all. But everywhere else in science except in quantum mechanics it is still possible, as we have seen, to interpret statistical behavior and probability merely as evidence of an incomplete understanding of a complex situation which if fully understood would not involve them. Hence, it is really the uncertainty principle which is responsible for introducing historical time into science.

The relation of historical time to providence

Unlike science the Bible is, however, almost exclusively concerned with historical time. The great Biblical themes of responsibility, freedom, and decision; of sin, salvation, and judgment;

of creation, redemption, and the *eskaton* all lose their meaning and content in a world in which the only kind of time is scientific time. Indeed, perhaps it is just here in the distinction between scientific time and historical time that the primary source of tension between science and religion is to be found. So long as science employed scientific time exclusively the world of science necessarily seemed a world apart from and alien to the Biblical world in which historical time is the primary reality. In the previous chapter we found in chance and accident the key element through which scientific law and Biblical providence can operate together without contradiction in the total determination of events. But since it is through chance and probability that historical time has entered science, we could equally well have put it that the world revealed by science as governed by the laws of nature, and the world revealed by the Bible as governed by the will of God could not be seen as a single reality until science incorporated historical time along with scientific time in an essential and determining way. This, however, is just another way of expressing the close connection between chance and probability on the one hand and the distinction which we have made between the two kinds of time on the other.

Chance and accident in the miracle of the exodus

A matter closely related both to the nature of chance and the distinction we have made between the two forms of time is that of the nature of miracle. In its broadest terms a miracle is an event which is apprehended by a worshipping community as a clear instance of the divine activity in the shaping of history. The question as to whether the event so apprehended does or does not violate known scientific laws is secondary. Our discussion here will be confined to miracles which do not violate any known scientific laws, but consist instead of events which, objectively considered, are either singular or extraordinarily improbable. An example of the former is the Incarnation or the Resurrection of our Lord, while the miracle of the exodus is a key example of the latter. It is this latter type of miracle which is intimately associated with the relationship between chance and providence which is our concern in this book.

The miracle of the exodus from Egypt was a central turning point in the history of Israel, and a crucial act in the sequence of historical events through which God's revelation of Himself to Israel was made. As can be seen from all of her subsequent literature in the Bible, no other single event in the whole history of Israel made anything like the impact which this providential deliverance made on this people. The miracle of the exodus therefore merits special attention in any discussion of the Biblical view of providence.

It will be well to base our consideration of this event and its implications on the earliest version of it which can be recovered from the present Biblical text. In securing such a version I have chosen to follow the analysis of C. A. Simpson, taking the account from what he calls the J_1 source of the Pentateuch.[2] Even so this version was not written down until perhaps three centuries after the event:

"(Exodus 13:21) And Yahweh went before them by day in a pillar of cloud, and by night in a pillar of fire. (22) The pillar of cloud by day and the pillar of fire by night did not

[2] Simpson, C. A., *Early Traditions of Israel*. Blackwell, Oxford, 1948, pp. 433-435.

depart from before the people. . . . (14:5) When the king of Egypt was told that the people had fled, (6) he made ready his chariot . . . (19) and the pillar of cloud moved from before them, and stood behind them, (20) and darkness (fell), and the night passed without one coming near the other all night. (21) And Yahweh drove the sea back by a strong east wind all night, and made the sea dry land. (24) And in the morning watch Yahweh in the pillar of cloud looked down upon the host of the Egyptians, and discomfited the host of the Egyptians. . . . (27) And the sea returned to its wanted flow when the morning appeared; and the Egyptians fled into it; . . . (28) not so much as one of them remained. (15:20) Then Miriam took a timbrel in her hand; and all the women went out after her with timbrels and dancing. (21) And Miriam sang to them:

'Sing to Yahweh, for he has triumphed gloriously;
The horse and his rider he has thrown into the sea!' "

The story, in this earliest form which is capable of being recovered, presents a rather different picture of this crucial event than the one we are familiar with from the final version in the Bible. A group of Israelites in flight from a captivity in Egypt are pursued by a contingent of Egyptian forces. In the excitement and uncertainty of the flight they are given heart by the assurance of Yahweh's presence with them through the vision of the volcano (the pillar of cloud by day and of fire by night) as seen perhaps in a storm cloud reminiscent of Sinai. So their God Yahweh, the god of the volcano and the storm, is present, observing their danger and ready to act in His power on their behalf. As night falls both those in flight and those pursuing find themselves along the shore of a shallow estuary (the sea of reeds), and both groups make camp there. During the night a

storm comes up of such violence that the wind drains the bed
of the estuary. The Egyptians, knowing the Hebrew's God
Yahweh to be the god of the storm, are terrorized by this display
of His mighty wrath. After a sleepless terror-filled night, they
break camp the moment morning appears and flee across the
drained bed of the estuary where they are engulfed and drowned
by the returning waters. An exultant couplet, undoubtedly composed on the spot, attributes the extraordinary release and victory of the Israelites to Yahweh.

The story in this form is clearly an instance of one of history's
great, crucial, and destiny-filled accidents of which we all know
a number of other examples. At its occurrence and from then
on throughout their history it was spontaneously and unani-
mously recognized as a great and mighty act of God on their behalf. So the story raises the problem of the nature of chance and
accident in history, and with it the associated problem of the
nature of miracle and its relationship to the Biblical view of
providence.

In discussing Washington's victory over Cornwallis at York-
town, which also resulted from the providential arrival of a
storm, Oscar Handlin in the book from which we have already
quoted makes a comment which can equally be applied to the
miracle of the exodus. It will illuminate the problem with
which we are presently concerned to quote this comment here:

> "In looking backward over the past, we do not wish to admit
> that we are ourselves the products of a series of accidents; we
> grope for some meaningful connection between the incidents
> that constituted the turning points and their surrounding cir-
> cumstances. Yet the causes of the former are independent of the
> causes of the latter. The atmospheric conditions that brought

on the storm and the military conditions that caused Cornwallis's army to retreat were the products of altogether separate chains of causes and effects. Was then their fateful convergence simply a contingency, unforeseeable and without meaning except in its results?"[3]

The application of this observation to the Biblical account of the exodus in its earliest form is obvious. If there had been an uninvolved observer from some distant land present at the exodus he might well have been able to see in the event nothing more than "a contingency, unforeseeable, and without meaning except in its results." The question which Handlin raises here is indeed the fundamental question which men down through the ages have posed to history. It brings us up abruptly against the elementary barrier of chance and accident in a way which makes especially clear the impenetrability of this barrier to the uninvolved objective observer of science. Yet the very raising of the question implies the imperative we all feel for penetrating this barrier in some way. Whatever the scientific analysis of the situation may produce in the way of probabilities, the event itself remains significant and determinative. The question as to the source of its significance remains insistently present.

Significant events in science and in the Bible

In order to answer this question it will be helpful first to consider the criteria which make an event significant and to contrast these criteria as they apply in science and in the Bible. Each of us is immersed in a sea of events which at every moment are occurring all about us and in us with tumultuous frequency and

[3] *Chance or Destiny: Turning Points in American History,* p. 192.

great variety. The sum total of all events which take place at any given moment is staggering in its immensity. Out of this total the number of which we can even be aware is only a minute fraction. Things happen in such profusion and so rapidly that we are scarcely able to keep up with them. So we are forced to "edit" out most of the events which happen as being trivial, unimportant, or of no concern to us. Like the editor of a newspaper, we sift through the kaleidoscopic profusion of happenings and screen from them a small number of "headline" items which we regard as significant and important. In order to do this at all, however, we must each have a set of criteria by which we can screen from the profusion of all events the particular and special ones which possess this significance. Usually we are entirely unconscious of the nature or even the existence of these criteria, and we apply them to the sifting process as automatically as we maintain the beating of our hearts or the process of breathing.

The problem of miracle in contemporary thought seems to me to have its roots in the nature of these subconscious criteria of significance. Specifically it arises from a radical difference between the Biblical criteria by which an event is determined to be significant and the criteria peculiar to science which make events significant. The Bible, as we have seen, is the literary expression of a people whose whole life and history are lived out in a consciously experienced intimate relationship or covenant with the living God. For such a people every event, known or unknown, trivial or important, forgotten or recorded, is an expression of His will. For them as for everyone, however, the tumultuous profusion of events is such that this aspect is not apparent or discernible in the great majority of them. Only occasionally and indeed rarely does an event occur in such a manner or in such a context that this aspect stands out clearly and unmistakably. When this is the case it is called a miracle. But from the Biblical standpoint a miracle is not a special kind of event possessing a quality which common happenings do not share. It is rather an occasion in which the essentially providential character of all events is made manifest in an especially clear and striking manner.

Science on the other hand consists in man's quest for understanding and insight into the basis of order and coherence in the world. From the standpoint of science an event is important and significant only insofar as it exemplifies some timeless universal principle. The great events in the history of science are the crucial experiments or key discoveries which in their time opened new vistas and unanticipated avenues of understanding by which fresh insights into the basis for order and coherence in the structure of things have been gained. From the standpoint of science every event, however trivial, unimportant, or common it may seem, must nevertheless have taken place in accordance with the laws of nature. The great majority of events, however, do not occur in such a way as to make this aspect evident. It is only within the life and experience of the scientific community, and then only through carefully designed experiments and the skill of the trained investigator, that the event which reveals some new law or order in the universe emerges and can be recognized for what it exemplifies.

In both scientific and Biblical thought the events which stand out with a peak significance, the great discoveries, have this property because of the clarity with which they illuminate the underlying character of every event. The great event in either case is not set apart in significance because of some unique feature which ordinary occurrences do not possess. On the contrary, it is precisely in its power to make manifest that which has been present, though unrecognized, all along that its significance lies. The miracle of the exodus was never for Israel an isolated act of a God who normally was not involved in human history. It was instead forever after a clear and decisive guarantee of the providential presence of God in every situation.

This brings us to the statement of a point of contrast which has great significance for our present inquiry. The more a given event has the power to reveal some timeless universal property of the world, the less it is capable of making manifest the hand of God in the shaping of events. And conversely, the more an event or sequence of events makes manifest the providential character of history, the more chaotic and fortuitous they will appear to those who seek only to discover universal law and order in history. Galileo's discovery of the laws of freely falling bodies led to great new insights into both the nature of inertia and the character of gravity, but a freely falling body reveals nothing of providence. The miracle of the exodus on the other hand was a potent revelation of the power of Yahweh to save His people, but objectively considered it can only seem an unlikely and fortuitous combination of special meteorological conditions which tell us nothing about the universal determinants of history in general. It is this mutual exclusiveness which accounts for much of the latent antagonism between scientific and Biblical thought. The Bible is quite uninterested in the discovery of the underlying ordered structure of things and the universal laws by which nature operates. As a result, the criteria which it employs for the selection of significant events screens out only what seems trivial and fortuitous to science and rejects all events which science regards as important. In like manner the criteria of significance employed by science automatically reject every evidence of God's activity in history and select only events which Biblically speaking are wholly non-revelatory in character. Small wonder, therefore, that the very idea of miracle is an anathema to science and that Biblical and scientific categories of thought stand in such tension.

In actual fact, however, both criteria of selection tend to exclude an aspect of reality and conceal the truth. Events in themselves share in both realities of order and providence. The enigma of history resides in the fact that every event is at one and the same time the result of the operation of universal natural laws and the object of the exercise of the divine will. As history unfolds, the world moves forward in accordance with the inner requirements of its structure and the universal laws to which it is subjected. This structure is, however, so constituted and the laws under which it operates so framed as to open innumerable alternatives. Among the chances and accidents of those alternatives history threads its amazing course, ever responsive to the mighty will of the Creator and Sustainer of history and expressing in the story which it tells the mysterious working out of His hidden purpose. Because of this it is possible either to assert that all events without exception are subject to the universal laws of nature and to sift out of the profusion of events those which make manifest the universal scope of this assertion, or to assert with equal validity that all events without exception are responsive to the will of Almighty God and to sift out of the profusion of events those which make manifest His universal sovereignty.

The relation of miracle to scientific laws

The majority of the Biblical miracles are, like that in the exodus, the result of an extraordinary and extremely improbable combination of chance and accident. They do not, on close analysis, involve, as is so frequently supposed, a violation of the laws of nature. Thus, for example, in the majority of the miracles of healing the physico-chemical, physiological, or psychological changes taking place in the body of the person healed could all have well occurred individually in full conformance with the scientific laws governing such processes. The healing resulted from the extremely improbable circumstance that they all occurred together in just the right way to produce the final result. No objective application of known medical or psychotherapeutic principles could have brought on the particular combination of processes required for the healing, but this does not mean that any one of them violates any of the laws known to medicine or psychotherapy. It simply means that scientific criteria are helpless to account for the extraordinary consequence of so many highly improbable developments in a single event. But, as we have already seen, scientific criteria are simply inapplicable to this kind of event. Only by going to the very different Biblical criteria for determining the significance of events can any insight into its meaning be had.

Even within the Biblical context, however, there is a strong tendency to give to the miraculous happening an objective validity independent of the response of the worshipping community to the presence and action of God in their life and history. This can be done by modifying the account of it so as to make its occurrence, objectively considered, not merely extraordinarily improbable but definitely impossible as an event in the natural order. This can be seen in the later versions of the story of the exodus, in which it ultimately acquired a character in complete violation of the laws of nature, with the added words "and made the sea dry land, and the waters were divided. And the people of Israel went into the midst of the sea on dry ground, the waters being a wall to them on their right hand and on their left" (Exodus 14:21,22). It is possible that all accounts of Biblical miracles which involve occurrences necessarily violating natural laws are the result of this tendency for late elaborators of the story of the event to guarantee its miraculous character. This tendency is a thoroughly natural one, arising as it does out of the normal desire of men to escape the requirement of knowing God only as He has chosen to reveal Himself within a community of response which requires an act of faith and commitment on the part of those who would share its life. Our Lord Himself recognized this desire and attested to its futility when, in response to the Pharisees who came to Him argumentatively seeking from Him a sign from heaven, He said, "Why does this generation seek a sign? Truly, I say to you, no sign shall be given to this generation" (St. Mark 8:11,12). The essence of miracle is lost when it reveals a reality in which ordinary events cannot partake. It then becomes nothing more than a "sign or wonder" which tells us nothing of the regular involvement of God in the scheme of things. Men in their faithlessness and desire for objective certainty independent of their own capacity for response to God will doubtless continue to demand such events as a condition of their belief, but it may well be, as our Lord Himself has assured us, that they will nevertheless not be given such "signs and wonders."

Some events by their very nature are singular, and hence not members of a class which can be made the object of scientific investigation by experimentally repeating them over and over at will. A singular event may or may not be miraculous depending on whether it does or does not reveal clearly the presence and action of God within the community to whom God is known. It may be, even for the community, merely a strange and remarkable phenomenon without any evident meaning or significance. But if for the community it does have clear and unmistakable significance, then it may well be a miracle, even though it does not involve any chance or accidental congruence of familiar or repeatable phenomena. Such, for example, are the miracles of the Creation, the Incarnation, and the Resurrection. These are singular events which were also charged with tremendous revelatory power. With respect to them it is meaningless to speak of either chance or accident. How would one go about assigning a probability to the occurrence of the universe, or to the event in which "the Word was made flesh and dwelt among us, so that we beheld his glory"? We can only speak of chance in terms of events which can happen repeatedly in alternative ways. But a singular event is neither repeatable nor are any alternatives to it, other than its not happening at all, open. Such events neither conform to nor violate natural law because their singularity precludes their repetition in accordance with any kind of pattern. There is no way to experiment with them in order to see whether they do or do not manifest any kind of regularity capable of being described scientifically.

It is an error to think of a miracle as being "unnatural." Chance and accident as well as the singular enter into and make up history just as much as do scientific, economic, and sociological laws. The miraculous is as much a part of the nature of history as the coherent. If a miraculous event could only happen outside the natural order of things, then it would necessarily imply that it would be unnatural for God to exercise providence over His creation. Such an idea is, however, clearly un-Biblical and contrary to everything which has been revealed of God in either Israel or Christ.

There is an insistent and recurring demand for some way of objectively establishing the fact of God and the reality of His providential activity apart from His self-revelation through Israel, Christ, and the Church. This, however, is a futile hope and the end of such a quest can only be frustration. It is analogous to a demand for acquiring scientific knowledge independently of observation and experiment and in a state of alienation from the spirit, discipline, and traditions of science. The only way to penetrate the elementary barrier of chance, accident, and the singular at which science in common with all purely experimental knowledge must stop, is to enter into and share the life of that special community of response within which God has been revealed. Only by so doing can men be set free to respond to the Biblical view of reality and to enjoy once more its revelatory and interpretive power. The Bible opens our eyes to behold the living God as He has revealed Himself in act and deed in historic events, "with a mighty hand and an out-stretched arm." Once we have seen Him and known Him as the people who have borne witness to us through the Bible saw and knew Him, there can be for us no longer any mere contingency or meaningless accident in events. From then on we acquire the gift to share their power of seeing His hand in every event. Sometimes, indeed, it will be seen in the terrible working out of His righteous judgment, as well as in the miraculous power of His saving and redeeming mercy. But whether in judgment or in redemption, His power will thereafter be known as a living and wonderful reality, transforming the chances and accidents of history into a glorious hope.

5

THE PARADOX OF FREEDOM
AND PROVIDENCE

Up to this point in this book we have said very little about the subject of freedom. Yet the notions of freedom and providence are inextricably bound up in each other. Moreover, their inter-relationships are of a fundamentally paradoxical nature. Only by examining thoroughly the character and structure of this relationship and exhibiting fully the nature of the paradoxes which are involved can the full implications of the Christian idea of providence be made evident. This will be our primary concern in this chapter.

The paradox between freedom and providence arises quite simply in the following way. If we assert that any given sequence of events involving a succession of free choices among alternatives is providential and took place in the manner in which it did because God willed that it should, we seem to imply that each separate act of choice could not really have been free at all. At each turning point in the sequence God must have acted in a determinative way in order that the sequence in question might form the pattern which He willed that it should, rather than any of the other patterns which the combinations of all available alternatives would allow. As soon as we have asserted this, however, have we not also asserted that what seemed to be chance or accident in the events concerned was not really so at all? When God exercises His providence in history, what happens to probability as a measure of valid alternative? Are we saying that God enters into situations which are the object of His providence and directs that particular choices be made in accordance with His purpose? But if so, are we not really committing ourselves to assert that chance and accident in history are illusory? Are what seem to be free choices among bona fide alternatives not really free after all, but directed by an unseen hand? And is what seems an accident not accidental after all, but a planned and intended coincidence brought about to achieve the unseen purpose?

These questions, of course, raise the old problem of predestination. Does God really know in advance in complete detail everything which is going to happen? Are we not committed to answer in the affirmative, if we believe that history is an expression of His will and purpose? But when we adopt any such position we seem to be denying that any real choice exists anywhere. If it can be known, by God or in any other way, what I shall decide to do tomorrow in a situation not known to me now, then I am not responsible for my decision and have no freedom at all to choose among the alternatives which will then present themselves to me. It would seem that a thoroughgoing doctrine of predestination would make mere puppets of us all, and of everything else in creation, too, with no choice really but to do what the divine manipulator directs.

Considerations such as these make us inclined to reject predestination as being wholly false to reality as we know it. Yet before we yield so quickly before such arguments, we must ask how far we are to go in preserving the integrity of choice, freedom, and responsibility in order to obtain a logically consistent view of the world. The end point of arguments conducted along this line, in which the preservation of this integrity is the controlling factor in determining their validity, can only be to push God out of history entirely. This we saw in several ways in the last chapter. When the reality of chance is asserted and defended by giving it the full connotation of "pure chance" and that of accident by giving it the full connotation of "mere happenstance," then any idea of destiny and providence fades away. Choice, freedom, and responsibility are, to be sure, vivid realities of raw human experience, and no argument, however neat and foolproof, which forces us into the corner of admitting that they must be only illusions is ever acceptable. But, on the other hand, destiny, grace, and purpose both in individual life and in history are equally vivid realities of human experience, and every argument which forces us into the opposite corner of admitting that they are illusions is equally unacceptable. Thus, although we seem to be unable to discover any rational way in which both of these realities could possibly be true at the same time, we must nevertheless affirm them both together.

In either science or theology, or indeed in any other area of rational inquiry, the stubborn facts of experience are always overriding. Any rational or theoretical argument, no matter how attractive and convincing it may be, which fails to do justice to the facts, must be abandoned. This is the case we are confronted with here. The paradox of freedom and providence is a real paradox. Throughout the history of philosophy it has baffled every effort to dissolve it by rational means. Indeed it is just the sturdy impregnability of this paradox against every theoretical assault which makes the elementary barrier of chance and accident in history a true barrier behind which man cannot probe with any instrument at his disposal, scientific or otherwise.

The paradox in non-Christian philosophy

The primary concern with this paradox is, of course, with the effort to gain as full an insight as possible into the Christian idea of providence. But it will assist us toward a fuller realization of our goal to pause at this point and take note of the universal character of the paradox in all fields of thought, Christian and non-Christian alike. For even in completely secular or pagan thought, from which providence in the Judeo-Christian sense is completely absent, the paradox nevertheless arises with just as much force. It is very evident, for example, in any system of mechanistic or naturalistic determinism, where in a light but nevertheless revealing vein we may take note of it through Dorothy Sayers' wonderful remark that "even the most thoroughgoing philosophic determinist will swear at the maid like any good Christian when the toast is burned." Mechanistic determinism is, in fact, the equivalent, for this problem, of divine predestination. Both are systems in which the die is already cast for the future and everything which is ever going to happen is already foreordained. In one case all future states of the universe are rigorously determined by a closed impersonal system of laws of nature in accordance with which there is only one way each element of nature can behave in each given set of circumstances. In the other case exactly the same result is achieved through the purpose and power of God who imposes upon all creation a rigid conformance to His will and intention for it. In either case the analogy introduced earlier to the completed picture being slowly revealed by the moving curtain is applicable. Chance, decision, and responsibility are then illusory, and we who think we are actors in the drama of life are in reality mere spectators of a play which has already been written in complete detail from beginning to end.

The moment the implications of a thoroughgoing determinism are presented in this way, either in its mechanistic or its predestinarian forms, the great majority of people will immediately reject it as untrue no matter how complete or weighty the arguments in favor of the theory may be. It is indeed a practical impossibility to act on the basis of such a thoroughgoing determinism regardless of the extent to which it may be theoretically believed to be true. Even Einstein, who, as we have seen, has given us in the Theory of Relativity a complete theoretical determinism of this sort, could not himself regard the rise of the Nazis in his native land in such terms, and his later years were filled with a profound sadness over the release of the Pandora's box of atomic energy to which he himself had contributed and with respect to which he felt a deep sense of personal responsibility. He was forced to treat his fellows as free agents capable of being dissuaded from one course of action and persuaded to another. Indeed, determinists are known to speak as passionately as other men on behalf of their ideas, treating thereby the choices and decisions of others as valid options in which alternatives are really present, and selections among them of vital importance. So, too, with the most thoroughgoing pre-destinarian preacher with a staunch belief in doctrines which adhere to the most rigorous interpretation of election and fore-ordination. Such a one will be found, nevertheless, exhorting his congregation to repentance, amendment of life, and conver-sion just as though each of them were really free to decide moral questions for themselves and capable of assuming full moral responsibility for the acceptance or denial of our Lord's call.

The paradox in the criminal law

The paradoxical element in this situation is nowhere so evi-dent as in the problem of crime and punishment as it appears in the criminal law. In jurisprudence modern secular and positivist ideas of behavioral determinism meet a practical test in which the necessities of social life demand the development of a work-able solution with such urgency that the issues involved cannot be simply bypassed in the interest of maintaining some theo-retical solution. The criminal law which our age inherited from the past was based on a recognition of personal responsibility in the full sense of classical moral theology as determined by the standard of the natural law. Into this situation the influence of the prevailing determinism of the late nineteenth and early twentieth centuries entered with disastrous effect. With the growth of psychology and sociology as scientific disciplines, the limitations imposed on human action by inheritance, training, and social and economic conditioning were emphasized to the exclusion of factors of moral choice and the responsible exercise of freedom. More and more in this environment the idea arose that the criminal is a helpless product of inherited weaknesses and adverse social conditioning. The question as to whether the criminal could have acted other than he did was thereby introduced into criminal law. It inevitably carried with it a revolution in thought concerning the basis on which that law rested.

If men are free and responsible agents, then one who freely chooses evil instead of good is morally blameworthy and his punishment under the penal law is justified. But if his choice of evil instead of good was an inevitable consequence of an inherited weakness coupled with past environmental conditioning, then his evil act was no choice at all but the only response he could have made in the circumstances in which he found himself. In this case any idea of punishment or retribution must be abandoned, and some other basis found for the law. There are three broad possibilities for such a basis and all of them have been employed in practice. First there is the positive basis of rehabilitation in which the judgments and penalties of the law are imposed on the wrongdoer with the objective of changing and eventually rehabilitating him. Under this system society assumes responsibility for the effects of adverse social conditioning on the criminal and seeks to design a penal system which will apply positive pressures and influences sufficient to counteract these effects and restore the criminal to normal life. The second basis is neutral, and regards the criminal law as existing simply for the protection of society. The penal system in this case is designed merely to deprive the criminal of further opportunity for crime. The third basis is the negative one of using the law as a restraining force on the rest of society. Under this system criminals are used by society to produce an environment in which crime is made so dangerous and fearful that the criminal tendencies in all of us are held in check. In this case punishment is meted out to the criminal not for his own good or for the protection of society, but only for its effect in frightening others who might otherwise be inclined to do as he did. Even though his crime was inevitable for him, the penal code nevertheless prescribes a severe punishment for his act. This punishment is a sacrifice of the criminal in order to secure the common good of society at large.

So long as the law had a purely moralistic basis and ignored all factors of hereditary weakness and social conditioning, it was unreal, insensitive and cruel. The recognition of the importance and relevance of these factors has been a great constructive force in our time and has led to many urgently needed reforms in our penal system. At the same time, however, every attempt to go the whole way with the criminal law by trying to exclude from it every element of freedom and responsibility has ended in failure. In actual practice neither the courts nor society at large can avoid facing up to the stark reality of moral responsibility. In spite of the reality and power of every external influence which molds our life, the plain fact is that we are still faced with choices and that there is no escape from the terrible necessity of making decision out of the depths of our freedom. Nowhere does the paradox of freedom and grace emerge so strongly and firmly as it does in the criminal law. The reason is that although we easily yield to the temptation to believe in a theory, on one or the other side of the paradox, which seems to be able to eliminate it in a convincing way and provide us with a neat and clear-cut way of looking at things, the moment a judge or jury tries to apply such a theory to an actual case, the

practical requirements of justice soon make evident its inade-
quacies, and the paradox reappears in all its stubbornness.

A passage from John Galsworthy's novel *The Dark Flower*,
for which I am indebted to Schroedinger, puts this paradox in
a particularly cogent and illuminating way. It is concerned with
the scattered thoughts of a young lad at night as he reflects on
the events of the day:

> "But that was it—you never could think what things would be
> like if they weren't just what and where they were. You never
> knew what was coming, either; and yet when it came, it seemed
> as if nothing else ever could have come. That was queer—you
> could do anything you liked until you'd done it, but when you
> had done it then you knew, of course, that you must always have
> had to."[1]

Perhaps we have said the ultimate about this paradox when
we acknowledge with this young lad that it is simply "queer."
We are confronted by two primary realities neither of which
can be denied without doing serious violence to the raw facts
of human experience. On the one hand is the powerful and
inexorable sweep of history which carries us along whether we
will or no. We call it providence and destiny. For others it may
be only an inscrutable fate. But by whatever name it is called
it is clearly there; integral and coherent, imposing its necessities
upon us. On the other hand, there is the incoherence and indeterminism of freedom; the free choice thrusting into history
unexpectedly to upset and divert its smooth flow. We ask, "are
we the creatures or the creators of history?" thinking that it

[1] As quoted in E. Schroedinger, *Science and Humanism*, Cambridge University Press, 1951, p. 63.

must surely be possible to answer one way or the other. But the only answer which ever does justice to the facts simply affirms the paradox by assuring us that we are equally both together.

The paradox in the Bible

More than in any other single feature, the unique power and reality of the Bible resides in its capacity to give full scope and recognition to both of these realities of existence from a single vantage point. Other literature at some point or other beguiles us into trusting more in the reality of one side than the other, thereby hinting that there is a way out of the paradox. But the Biblical literature from beginning to end preserves it fully within a single, all-compassing view of reality. Nowhere is there any loophole provided for an escape from the terrible weight of the responsibility which freedom entails. Man, made in the image of God, shares in the freedom which God possesses. Man sins and his sin is imputed against him. In spite of the fall which makes sin inevitable, a man's sin is still his and there is no excusing it or passing it off as something he could not help. Sin incurs the wrath of God, and His judgment on all unrighteousness is sure and terrible.

The Bible, however, for all its uncompromising maintenance of the reality and fullness of human freedom and responsibility is just as uncompromising in the fullness with which it maintains the power and dominion of God over all of His creation and everything that happens within it. His purposes cannot be foiled by any act of man and His victory is assured. He is the source of every good and righteous motive that wells up in the heart of man, and from Him is derived every gift that man possesses including life itself. He is long-suffering, of great goodness, and His mercy endures forever. The whole of creation is His along with every incident and episode of its history. "He forms light and creates darkness, He makes weal and creates woe."[2] There is no escape from His judgment, yet the abundance of His mercy is ever open to all, saint and sinner alike, whenever they call upon Him and trust in His name.

The conclusion of the story of Joseph gives concrete expression to the fullness and depth of the Biblical view of freedom and providence, preserving the paradox, yet integrating both realities within a single comprehensive whole. After the death of their father Jacob, Joseph's brothers speak among themselves concerning the just recompense for their evil deed which awaits them now that the tables are turned and they are at the mercy of Joseph. They say, "It may be that Joseph will hate us and pay us back for all the evil which we did to him."[3] So they come to Joseph and fall down before him in abject submission. Joseph, however, rebukes them saying, "Fear not, for am I in the place of God? As for you, you meant evil against me; but God meant it for good, to bring it about that many people should be kept alive, as they are today."[4]

In this brief exchange we have an epitome of the Biblical understanding of freedom and providence. Both Joseph and his brothers recognize together the objective fact of the latters' evil act. For Joseph it had meant a period of agony and anguish. Like a bolt out of the blue it had destroyed all of the bright prospects of his young life. A prince joyfully awaiting the fruition of a rich inheritance suddenly had found himself a slave in a foreign

[2] Isaiah 45:7
[3] Genesis 50:15
[4] Genesis 50:19, 20

land at the mercy of a wandering band of alien Bedouins. The brothers on their part had planned this vicious act with full knowledge of its nature and gravity. They had freely consented to evil, recognizing it fully for what it was. "As for you, you meant evil against me." There is no excusing or explaining away the reality of responsibility here on either side. The evil act once performed stands out starkly for what it is. No amount of abject submission can remove the guilt of it, nor could any revenge which Joseph might now take on his brothers alter the fact of it.

The purposes of God, however, are not foiled by the wickedness of men. If they were, who could bear the burden of his guilt? So Joseph's answer to his brothers consists in turning their attention with his to the, in Handlin's neat phrase, "miraculous streak of luck which at one turning point after another had directed fortune his way" until finally the present outcome has been realized of "bringing it about that many people should be kept alive, as they are today." Here clearly is the certain evidence of the mighty providence of God mysteriously emerging from a long sequence of chances and accidents, working wonderfully in and through history to transform and redeem the damage and hurt wrought in the world by the evil acts of sinful men and in the end accomplishing far more than could ever have been expected or hoped for. Joseph and his brothers are alike humbled by the realization of God's presence in all these events. In consequence they are, as the story tells us, reassured and comforted by this insight. For the brothers it meant the amazing discovery that the damage done in the world by their evil deed does not have to remain there forever accusing them. The fact of it and the guilt of it remain, of course, but not the awful burden of it.

For one mightier than they, mightier even than the combined powers of all creation, has, as all can now see, meant for good that which they had meant for evil. For Joseph, on the other hand, the very thought of revenge would be a terrible presumption in the light of such a recognition. Who indeed would he be to presume now to enter in and tamper with a situation which one so much mightier than he had already taken over and brought out to such a glorious conclusion? So together they are reassured and comforted as they gratefully leave the matter in God's hands with Joseph's simple words, which so perfectly express the paradox of freedom and providence, "As for you, you meant evil against me, but God meant it for good."

The paradox in the Christian life

This Biblical view of God's action and man's freedom rises to its most decisive and conclusive peak in the great central and climactic event of Calvary. There in the humble nobility of the lonely figure of the "Word made flesh and dwelling among us" in the presence of the howling mob shouting with hot and bitter anger for His crucifixion, we see the terrible reality of human freedom at its worst. Here "Him by whom all things were made," even the creator and preserver of those who now press about Him so hotly, is Himself the object of the most passionate desire for evil that human freedom can choose. Yet that freedom is preserved inviolate and allowed full reign and sway even to the point of crucifying to the death Him in whom all might, majesty, dominion, and power are pleased to dwell. How possibly could the freedom of man be maintained in conjunction with the providence and power of God more fully and completely than that? Yet as in the case of the evil done to Joseph, and indeed as in every situation involving man's freedom, the cross is only one side of the picture. For the cross led to the empty tomb and to Easter. There in the figure of the risen Christ is the ultimate sign and seal of God's triumph over the evil which men in their freedom let loose in the world. Here is a blinding glimpse into the innermost reality behind the mystery of history, and it is a vision of triumph, victory, and a sure and certain hope. Nowhere will we find the paradox of freedom and providence so fully and profoundly set forth and represented as in the combined symbol of the cross and the empty tomb.

It lies at the very heart of the Christian life that it is a way of living which succeeds in giving full expression to both human freedom, initiative, and responsibility and to an absolute dependence on and trust in the grace and providence of God, within one and the same life. No more illuminating or impressive example of this can be found than that of the life of St. Paul himself. Over and over he finds it necessary to maintain the paradox in order to preserve the fullness and reality of the good news. To those who had thought the essence of true religion to be in man's effort to live by the law, St. Paul maintains that this effort can only end in inducing a more profound consciousness of his sinfulness and essential unrighteousness. To those who strive to make themselves acceptable before God through good works and deeds and believe that therein lies the essence of true religion, St. Paul maintains that the simple act of faith in Christ is the only route by which any real sense of justification before God can be had. To those who take it for granted, along with the overwhelming weight of all religious opinion, that man must first reform and purify himself before he can become worthy of God and reap the benefits of the religious life, St. Paul points to the astounding fact of God's out-reaching love for the most miserable sinners:

> "While we were yet helpless, at the right time Christ died for the *ungodly* . . . while we were yet *sinners* Christ died for us."[5]

The very heart of this message is summed up in that great passage from Ephesians:

> "For by grace you have been saved through faith; and this is not your own doing, it is the gift of God—not because of works, lest any man should boast. For we are his workmanship, created in Christ Jesus for good works, which God prepared beforehand, that we should walk in them."[6]

But this message abounds with problems which arise from our central paradox of freedom and providence. Unless the element of paradox is understood there is danger of missing its full truth and validity. Thus, in his letter to the Romans in which St. Paul strives to work out the full implications of this central reality of the Christian life, he finds it periodically necessary to interrupt his argument in order to deal with questions whose origin is simply the conviction that there can be either freedom or providence but not both together in paradox. For example:

> "Do we then overthrow the law by this faith? By no means! On the contrary, we uphold the law."[7]
>
> "What shall we say then? Are we to continue in sin that grace may abound? By no means! How can we who died to sin still live in it?"[8]
>
> "What then? Are we to sin because we are not under the law but under grace? By no means! . . . But thanks be to God, that

[5] Romans 5:6, 8 (author's italics).
[6] Ephesians 2:8-10
[7] Romans 3:31
[8] *Ibid.* 6:1, 2

you who were once slaves of sin have become obedient from the heart to the standard of teaching to which you were committed, and, having been set free from sin, have become slaves of righteousness."[9]

This last is followed by the frank acknowledgment of the paradox involved when he says, "I am speaking in human terms, because of your natural limitations."[10] In another place the paradox appears in a way which makes it stand out most clearly and sharply defined of all in his characteristic phrase, "I . . . : yet not I, but the grace of God which was with me."[11] Here we have it in its most elementary simplicity. Freedom on its side asserts all that "I" in the free exercise of my will have chosen, done, and accomplished. But immediately providence on its side of the paradox enters and calls forth the denial "yet not I, but the grace of God working in me." Neither the proposition nor its denial can be omitted without doing violence to the facts. The Christian life is like that, and any purely rational simplification of it which seeks to make one of the two elements dominant at the expense of the other simply fails to take account of all the facts of that life.

Because this central fact of the Christian life is a paradox, the Church has always found it difficult to maintain it in its doctrinal formulations. What it has usually done as an alternative has been to side with providence against freedom. This, however, has never been in practice a denial of the paradox but rather a merely practical way of assuring that the paradox will be at least approximately maintained. For as a practical matter

[9] *Ibid.* 6:15, 17, 18
[10] *Ibid.* 6:19
[11] I Cor. 15:10

when the centrality of grace is asserted by maintaining that no salvation can be had in any way apart from God's action, the Church can be sure that its people will continue to be exhorted to reform and strive for uprightness simply because of the vividness of our own sense of freedom and the inevitability of the effort which men can be counted upon to exert in order to persuade their fellows. When, on the other hand, the centrality of the human will is emphasized against the necessity of grace in order to preserve the worthiness and value of the effort to lead a good and virtuous life, the reverse is not true. In that case, providence and grace quickly fade out and the Christian life rapidly degenerates into a mere moralism.

This, it seems to me, is the basis for the decision of the Church in favor of St. Augustine against Pelagius. In practice it did succeed in preserving the paradox even though the stated position would seem to eliminate man's role in the process completely and thus to deny any reality at all to man's exercise of moral responsibility in freedom. Later in the Reformation this again constituted the basis for the radical reintroduction of providence and grace as essential elements of the Christian life. Yet neither Luther with his strong emphasis on salvation by faith nor Calvin with his emphasis on predestination and election really denies the paradox. In either case, the practical effect of even a rigorous adherence to these doctrines is to achieve some approach to the Pauline position. The Church in the century just preceding the Reformation and again the Church of the nineteenth-century enlightenment from which we are just now emerging are, on the other hand, convincing examples of the way in which all evidence of providence and grace can be lost from the Christian life when the opposite position is taken.

An analogous paradox in physics

The paradox of freedom and providence seems to be in-grained in the very nature of things. Certainly every attempt so far to find a rational resolution of it has failed in spite of the fact that this has always been a crucial problem in philosophy, and the history of such attempts is a long and determined one. In more recent times the growth of scientific modes of thought about reality has resulted in renewed attacks on the problem. The idea of a real or irremovable paradox has seemed partic-ularly intolerable in science, and this one in particular has been assaulted with vigor by the newly developing sciences of psy-chology and sociology. Yet in spite of the magnitude of the fresh effort from this new vantage point, the paradox continues to stand as unassailable and impregnable as ever.

The experiences of the last thirty years in physics which have already been referred to in the second chapter can provide con-siderable insight into the nature of paradox. It will help us greatly in arriving at a new orientation with respect to the para-dox of freedom and providence to describe these experiences from the standpoint of what is called the Bohr Principle of Complementarity. This principle is itself one of the conse-quences of the Heisenberg Indeterminacy Principle, which, as we have already seen, is the basis on which quantum mechanics rests. It applies to an essential characteristic of the way in which physical systems are described in quantum mechanics which prior to quantum mechanics could only be regarded as an outright paradox. What it does, therefore, is to provide us with a con-crete example which can be subjected to detailed study of a situation which at first seemed necessarily paradoxical, but was discovered from a new vantage point to be capable of being viewed as representing complementary aspects of a single reality. It offers, as we shall see, a striking parallel to the paradox of freedom and grace, a parallel indeed which Bohr himself has already noted.[12]

In the second chapter we were concerned with the way in which the introduction of the Indeterminacy Principle into classical mechanics produced in physics statistical modes of description involving alternatives and probabilities. It is this aspect of quantum physics which is most relevant to the relationship between chance and providence which is our main concern in this book. There is, however, another equally striking aspect of quantum mechanics which has to do with contrasting ways in which the nature of physical systems is defined by quantum mechanics. The best known example of this is the wave-particle contrast in the nature of light, electrons, and other atomic or sub-atomic systems, but there are other examples as well. This contrast was already well defined experimentally before the advent of quantum mechanics and from the standpoint of classical physics constituted a crucial paradox which it was believed any satisfactory theory must somehow find a way of resolving.

Throughout the first quarter of this century a large amount of experimental information on the behavior of light and electrons was accumulated as many new techniques were developed and perfected. The history of this period of rapidly increasing information about the physical properties of such systems is one of increasing bafflement. The more precise and firmly grounded

[12] N. Bohr, "On Notions of Causality and Complementarity," *Science,* vol. III, January 20, 1950, concluding paragraphs on page 54.

this information became, the more paradoxical was the problem of its assimilation into a coherent and rational picture of the atomic world. Striking and apparently irreconcilable contradictions, instead of beginning to yield before the determined assault being made upon them, were rather more and more firmly established with each new step in research. Classical physics interpreted light as a wave phenomenon and regarded electrons as particles. We still today think of the radiation emitted from a radio broadcast antenna, which is just another form of the same radiation as light, as being an electromagnetic wave, and we tune our radio sets to receive it at a frequency of so many kilocycles per second or a wave length of so many meters. We certainly also think of electrons as particles with a definite mass and electronic charge, and as important building blocks of matter. In confirmation of these interpretations a large body of thoroughly convincing experimental evidence that light is indeed a wave phenomenon and that electrons are particles has been assembled. But, at the same time, there was accumulated an equally convincing and well-grounded body of experimental evidence which provides equally compelling proof that light consists of discrete particles and that electrons are true waves. Indeed, the photoelectric cells which make possible the sound tracks for our movies and the geiger counters used by uranium prospectors which click each time a particle of light-like radiation is absorbed in them would not work at all if light were not made up of real particles. On the other hand, much valuable information has been obtained on the structure of crystals by reflecting electron or neutron waves from them and measuring interatomic distances in terms of the electron or neutron wave length in the same way as with x-rays.

Thus, physics was faced with complementary sets of entirely convincing experimental evidence, each of which has by now led to many practical applications in operating devices, which are of such a character that each set proves the opposite of the other. One entirely convincing set of experiments proves that light and electrons are both particles, while another equally extensive and convincing set of experiments proves that they are both waves. Baffled physicists of the time, convinced that nature must somehow be so constituted as to require them to be either one or the other, sought by every conceivable means ways of discrediting or at least reinterpreting one or the other of these sets of experiments. The universal expectation was that ultimately we would find some satisfactory way of conceiving of light and electrons which would show them to be *really* particles with the capacity of somehow behaving like waves, or alternatively of being *really* waves with the capacity of behaving like particles. But no such way has been found, and the experimental evidence continues to stand as firmly and unassailable as ever.

It is to this apparently paradoxical situation that the Bohr Principle of Complementarity applies. It does so by asserting that it is of the essence of a world to which quantum mechanics applies that light, electrons, and other similar physical systems will have wave *and* particle properties as *complementary* aspects of a single reality. Thus, this principle asserts that the experimental situation is not to be regarded as a paradox capable of being resolved by further work, but rather looked upon as reflecting an essential characteristic of reality, associated with the uncertainty principle, as a result of which physical systems present themselves to our observation in complementary aspects.

The Principle of Complementarity

Some insight into the way in which the Principle of Complementarity operates in quantum mechanics can be gained by
thinking of the natural world as a photographic negative and of
our knowledge of the world as a print made from this negative.
The incompleteness of our knowledge of the world could be
represented in this analogy by an opaque film covering large
areas of the negative so that a print made from it at any time
would have large blank areas corresponding to parts of nature
not yet known. Here and there on it spotty patches of exposed
print would represent those parts of nature concerning which
we do have some knowledge. The task of scientific research is
to remove bit by bit portions of the obscuring film until ultimately all becomes known. In the infancy of science when very
little was known about the physical world, a print made from
this negative would be nearly blank. With the progress of
science successive prints made at different stages would have
larger and larger areas exposed, corresponding to the growth
of our knowledge. Other prints made from the negative in the
future would be expected to have still greater areas exposed.

Now classical physics regarded our scientific knowledge of
the world and the external entities and phenomena in nature
which were so known as being in a one-to-one correspondence
with each other. What was known in physics about the structure
and behavior of a planet or an atom was considered to be pos-
sessed by the thing itself. The positions, velocities, accelerations,
forces, masses, and energies which classical physics uses to describe things in the external world all have a direct reference
to something inhering in the world itself. This same relation-

ship would apply also to scientific knowledge in other fields. In terms of our analogy we could say that this direct one-to-one correspondence between the world and our scientific knowledge of it could be represented by a contact print. What shows on the print is an exact replica of that part of the natural world which is known at the time the print is made.

With this in mind we can understand something of the fundamental character of the revolution produced in physics when classical mechanics was converted into quantum mechanics by noting that this traditional relationship between our knowledge of the world and the world itself is radically altered in quantum physics. The alteration is of such a character that it is no longer possible to think of this relationship in terms of a contact print. Rather we have to think of a complex system of lenses placed between the negative and the photographic print which projects onto the print a modified and altered image of the picture on the negative. We can have on the print, representing what we can know about the world, not a direct image in one-to-one correspondence with the world, but only a kind of shadow pattern of reality. Thus, what quantum mechanics introduced into physics was not merely a different or alternative description of the structure and behavior of the external world, but more basically a radical modification in the relationship between the real world and our knowledge of the world.

In quantum mechanics every element of the real world—e.g., an electron, an atom, or a molecule—is represented by an abstract mathematical function. It has become customary to designate such a function by the Greek letter ψ (psi), and we can therefore refer to such a function simply as a psi-function. If, for example, we were interested in studying some problem about the structure and behavior of a water molecule (H_2O), we would as a first step have to construct such a mathematical function to represent the water molecule. This can be done in a perfectly definite way by means of certain rules of correspondence which define the precise manner in which psi-functions correspond to the real entities in the external world which they represent. In terms of our analogy, the water molecule itself is an object on the photographic negative, the psi-function is its shadow pattern on the print, and the rules of correspondence between them are determined by the intervening lens system which determines the nature of the image of reality which is projected onto the print.

The psi-functions themselves have no alternatives, probabilities, or indeterminacies associated with them. They are rigorously determined in their behavior by laws which form the substance of quantum mechanics. They exist exclusively in scientific time without past, present, or future. If the water molecule is subjected to certain well-defined forces in the real world, the psi-function representing it will change as time goes on in a completely causal and determined manner. For any given time in the future the equations of quantum mechanics allow one to compute just what the psi-function will be at that time. The solution is rigorously determined and there is only one answer. It is only when, after obtaining such a solution, one projects it back onto the water molecule in order to discover what the theory predicts will have happened to it in the meantime, that the indeterminacies, probabilities, and alternatives are reintroduced. Although the new psi-function representing the water molecule after it has been acted upon by known forces for the given period of time is perfectly definite and causally related to the initial psi-function, when it is projected back onto that which it represents, we find that the real water molecule may have responded to the forces acting on it in several alternative ways. The probabilities that each of these alternatives will have been selected in an actual situation are obtained when the rules of correspondence are applied to the psi-function representing the state of the water molecule after the forces have acted on it. In the second chapter we described how the solution of any physical problem in quantum mechanics differs from the corresponding solution of the problem in classical mechanics. The description just given shows more specifically how these differences actually work out in practice.

The distinction made in the preceding chapter between scientific time and historical time is relevant here. The real world is in historical time. The real entities or existences composing it exist in a present moment, a now. Each has a history which constitutes its past and an indeterminate future pregnant with alternative possibilities for it. Its "life" in time consists in the selection in each present moment of one of the alternatives coming to it out of the future and the abandonment of all others. In order, however, to study the structure or behavior of any such entity scientifically so as to uncover the invariable, timeless, and universal laws which govern it, it is necessary to remove all elements from it characteristic of historical time so as to deal only with an abstract residuum or framework incorporating everything about the entity in question which belongs only to scientific time. This is done by assigning to each open alternative in the future a numerical probability and then using the rules of correspondence to construct from such probabilities the appropriate psi-function. This process could be expressed in terms of our photographic analogy by saying that the negative which corresponds to the real entities existing in the external world is in both historical and scientific time. The lens system is then constructed in such a way as to screen out the elements belonging to historical time so that only the residuum belonging to scientific time will be projected on the print representing our scientific knowledge of the world.

With this analogy in mind we can now return to our original question of the meaning of the Principle of Complementarity. Here the important point is that the psi-function representing a ray of light, or an electron, or a neutron is neither a wave nor a particle. It is merely a definite, though abstract, mathematical function. In itself it exhibits no complementary features; not any more than it does indeterminacies or probabilities. It is only when it is projected back through the lens system onto the reality which it represents that both chance and probability on the one hand, and complementary features like the wave-particle aspects on the other, appear. Thus we cannot say whether the electron is either a wave or a particle. Everything which can be scientifically known about the electron is contained in the psi-function which represents it. This function, however, is quite different from either a wave or a particle. It is only as we project the information about the electron contained in the psi-function back onto the real electron which it represents that this question arises. When we do so, however, the rules of correspondence operate in such a way as always to exhibit both wave and particle properties in complementary relationship. In expressing complementarity as a fundamental principle of nature, Bohr was simply noting the fact that the rules of correspondence relating psi-functions with the realities which they represent always operate in such a way as to introduce complementary aspects.

Complementarity in fields other than physics

My purpose in devoting so much time to the Principle of Complementarity is not to suggest that it might apply directly to complementary situations in fields outside the domain of quantum physics. Specifically I do *not* believe, as I have emphasized already at the beginning of the second chapter, that the paradox of freedom and providence is a direct consequence of the Heisenberg indeterminacy principle. Rather, my purpose is to suggest that it may well be necessary in all other fields of science ultimately to introduce some kind of rules of correspondence which will remove the elements of historical time from the systems in nature which are the objects of scientific study in those fields. Whatever such rules were, their operation would result in some kind of scheme for representing entities in the real world by something abstract which pertained only to scientific time. This something would not be a psi-function and it might well not even be mathematical in expression. But it would represent an amoeba or a tree, an individual man or a human society through certain rules of correspondence in some way analogous to that in which a psi-function is used in quantum mechanics to represent an atom or a molecule. Put in another way, what we are suggesting is that there is no *a priori* reason why we should expect that our knowledge of the world must be in one-to-one correspondence with the real entities of the world in the way in which a contact print corresponds to the photographic negative from which it is made. Rather, because of the fact that everything which is exists in both historical and scientific time, we might well expect instead that our knowledge of the world must in every field of inquiry be related to the real world through some complex lens system which projects only a shadow pattern of reality from the negative onto the print.

If this should indeed be the case, then the analogy with the situation in quantum mechanics would suggest two consequences in the character of scientific knowledge in general. The first would be the introduction of chance and probability as an essential feature of all science, and the second would be the apprehension of reality in other scientific fields in complementary terms. Now we have already shown in the second chapter that chance and probability are indeed broadly characteristic of the way in which scientific results are expressed in all fields of investigation. The great suggestive power of classical mechanics as a model for ultimate achievement in scientific explanation continues even now to mask this simple fact so that it is not yet generally recognized or admitted. Nevertheless, the statistical character of scientific knowledge in all fields is an evident feature of it which attests to the indeterminacies and alternative modes of response involved in all existence in historical time. Thus one of the consequences of our supposition does seem to be realized in practice quite generally.

The other consequence by which we would expect reality to present itself to us in complementary terms also seems to be met in practice. One example in biology is the way in which mechanistic and vitalistic views of living organisms are used in a typically complementary fashion. In an entirely valid sense an organism can be looked upon as a physico-chemical system which behaves in certain well defined ways in response to external stimuli and environmental factors. But in another equally valid sense the same organism can be studied as a living unit which operates upon and modifies its environment in characteristic ways. Edmund W. Sinnott in the first portion of his book, *The Biology of the Spirit*,[13] gives a number of striking examples of such complementary aspects of living organisms. Elsewhere he has made and defended the complementary theses that man's body is as much the product of his mind as his mind is the product of his body. On the one hand, each individual begins as a single cell which thereafter, by an amazing sequence of processes, produces out of unorganized organic material coming to it a whole body. On the other hand, there is the physiological structure of the nervous system in which physico-chemical processes make mental activity possible. Indeed, the question as to whether the reality "man" is mind or body is remarkably reminiscent of the question whether the reality "light" is wave or particle. Perhaps the former may be a truly complementary situation in much the same way as the latter is known to be.

A related example can be found in the field of psychosomatic medicine which stands in a strictly complementary relationship to physiological and pharmacological methods in the therapy of mental disorders. Numerous examples of the effects of hormones and other biochemical factors as well as physiological defects on the mind and the personality can be cited to establish the physico-chemical basis of psychological phenomena. Just as numerous groups of equally well-attested examples can, on the other hand, be cited from psychosomatic medicine to establish the essentially psychological basis of physico-chemical processes in the body. Indeed, every physician can bear witness from his own experience to the determining role which the general

[13] Viking Press, 1955. Chs. II and III.

mental and spiritual tone of a patient plays in physiological healing and resistance to disease. When one listens to arguments among medical specialists as to whether psychotherapy or chemotherapy represents the more fundamental approach, the essentially complementary character of the situation becomes quite evident.

We have already noted the complementary character of history which arises from the circumstance that we are at one and the same time both creatures and creators of history. In one entirely valid sense we are the products of our inheritance and environment, while in an equally valid sense both our heritage and our contemporary environment are the result of human determination and effort. Any phenomenon in history can be and indeed always is treated in such a complementary way. Consider, for example, the phenomenon of the rise of the European national states. It is perfectly valid to speak of nationalism as a political and sociological force which produced and energized such figures as Cavour and Bismarck and in this way explain the rise of the national states as the result of nationalism. On the other hand, it is equally valid to point to the political leadership of such individuals as Cavour and Bismarck as the cause of the national states and so to make them ultimately responsible for the phenomenon of nationalism. The two approaches represent mutually exclusive modes of explanation whose equal validity places them in a complementary relationship to each other.[14]

[14] This example was suggested to me by the conclusion on pages 302-306 of the book *Realism and Nationalism, 1852-1871* by Robert C. Binkley (New York: Harpers, 1935) to which I was referred by a graduate student in history at Princeton University after he heard me give a lecture on complementarity. The entire book and especially this concluding portion will be found most illuminating in this context.

The application of the idea of complementarity to the paradox of freedom and providence should by now be evident. It is clear that the necessity, which we illustrated in a variety of ways in the first part of this chapter, for maintaining with equal force the reality of human responsibility for and divine determination of the course of events has all the characteristics of a truly complementary situation. Viewed from this standpoint St. Paul's central assertion, "I, yet not I, but the grace of God which was with me," can be recognized as the acknowledgment of a single reality which presents itself to our apprehension in complementary terms. From a strictly formal standpoint it still represents a logical paradox. But so too from a strictly formal standpoint does the assertion that light is both a wave and a particle represent a logical paradox. The solution in either case lies in first reorienting our thinking about the relationship between human knowledge and understanding on the one hand and the reality which we seek to know on the other. When we have done this properly we can understand how it could be that in the very nature of things the reality we designate as "light" or "electron" would present itself to our apprehension as both wave and particle in complementary relationship. In the same way we can understand how it could be that the nature of things would be such that the reality we call "decision" could present itself to our apprehension of it as both freedom and grace in complementary relationship. When we do this, however, we do not tend to speak of "paradox" any longer. The reason why we do not is that we have come to realize that the use of such a term implies an *a priori* commitment to a view of the relationship between knowledge and reality which may be overly simple and naive. Out of a more mature and profound view of this rela-

tionship we speak instead of complementarity, and thereby re-
nounce the requirement we would like to impose on reality that
it must meet all the demands of our formal logic before it can
qualify with us as something real.

6

THE TWOFOLD NATURE OF REALITY

The analysis which we have made so far of the Biblical idea
of providence within the context of contemporary scientific
thought has led us to formulate several fairly sharply defined
issues. Among these the most important is the barrier which
separates the Biblical recognition of providence on one side
from the scientific recognition of chance and accident on the
other. Although our analysis may perhaps have succeeded in its
objective of showing that these two apprehensions are simply
two sides of the same coin, or even better two images of the
same reality, it has not shown how the transition from one mode
of thought to the other can be made. There remains the question: how can the man who, being enmeshed in the scientific

thought forms of his age sees nothing beyond chance and accident in the shaping of events, be enabled to escape from his intellectual prison and helped over the barrier to the point where he is able to think Biblically about the same phenomena? It is toward the development of an answer to this basic question that this final chapter will be devoted.

The basis on which we will seek a resolution of this problem will be the exposition of a twofold character of reality which science by its very nature is incapable of discerning. We shall endeavor to show that reality stretches out before us in two distinct and sharply contrasted dimensions or worlds, and that Biblical thought is primarily, though not exclusively, concerned with one of these dimensions or worlds while science as such— though not the activity of engaging in science as a human pursuit —is exclusively confined to the other. Once this fundamental distinction has been made and clarified, it will then be possible for us to derive important insights into such matters as the paradox of freedom and grace, or the manner in which chance and accident is transmuted into Biblical providence.

The worlds of I *and* It *and of* I *and* Thou

The insights necessary for an exposition of this twofold character of reality have their origin in an important little book which constitutes one of the great milestones in recent religious thought, namely, Martin Buber's *I and Thou*.[1] What Buber recognizes so clearly and establishes so decisively in this book is that the whole of reality accessible to man lies within two worlds; not merely in one as we have become accustomed to believe. These worlds he calls the world of *I* and *It* and the

[1] Charles Scribner's Sons, 1937. Edinburgh, Messrs. T. & T. Clark, 1937.

world of *I* and *Thou*. Scientific knowledge, as we shall see, is necessarily confined to the world of *I* and *It*. This remains so even though the scientist himself may and often does move over into the world of *I* and *Thou* in his pursuit of scientific knowledge. Because of this such scientific notions as alternative, choice, probability, chance, and accident also belong to the world of *I* and *It*. The Bible, on the other hand, moves largely in the world of *I* and *Thou* and it is there that such primarily Biblical notions as freedom, grace, sacrifice, judgment, redemption, providence, and destiny have meaning and content. To exist wholly in the world of *I* and *It* is to live in a spiritual and intellectual prison from which everything distinctively Biblical has been excluded. The answer to our question of how to liberate the man dominated by scientific categories of reality from this prison so that he can see the hand of God in the shaping of events and at the same time know the reality of his own freedom, lies therefore in opening to his apprehension the possibility of this other world, the world of *I* and *Thou*.

Since Descartes, Western thought has been dominated by the relationship between a knowing, experiencing subject, the self, and the objects and events around him which he perceives and knows, namely, the observable world. In philosophy this relationship specifically gives rise to the epistemological problem, but more generally it has, with the single exception of more recent existentialist philosophies, constituted the exclusive domain within which the nature of reality has been considered. All reality in this mode of thought consists in "external" objects and events which are responsible for the perceptual experience of an observing subject. The real world is taken to consist of the sum total of objects and events which are capable in some way of entering into the perceptual experience of some observer by whom they can be known as objects or events of this world. It is just this world which Buber designates the world of *I* and *It*. It is the world constituted by the *I,* an experiencing and knowing subject, and the *It,* the things and phenomena which the *I* experiences and knows.

This dominating concern with the world of things and events reaches its most restrictive form in the case of science. By its very nature science must be exclusively concerned with the world of observable objects and events. The other world of the *I* and *Thou* which we shall shortly consider is wholly excluded from the scientific activity simply because anything capable of scientific investigation must first be reduced to observable entities and phenomena capable ultimately, by means of auxiliary objects and phenomena in the form of instruments, of producing perceptual experience in one or more scientific observers.

The remarkable triumphs of science over just the last fifty years have enormously expanded the range of human experience in the world of *I* and *It*. This world has become vastly extended in both space and time and has been peopled with objects and phenomena in enormous variety and number which were never before accessible to human apprehension. Both in the microcosm of the very small where elementary particles, atoms, molecules, genes, chromosomes, and micro-organisms have been unveiled, as well as in the macrocosm of the very large where giant stars, interstellar matter, galaxies, island universes, and supernovae have been revealed, the content of the observable world has been increased by many fold. But all these discoveries and triumphs, impressive as they assuredly are, are nevertheless exclusively an expansion of the world of *I* and *It*. Science in its totality and by its nature can only add to the content of the world of objects and phenomena which man knows or apprehends.

Over against this world of the *I* and *It* where science resides, is the world of pre-existent beings who meet each other across the void, not as objects of each other's experience, but as beings who share the fact of existence in common and meet on an equal basis and footing. It is not a substantial world possessing extent, duration, solidarity, and reliability. From the standpoint of science, which can do nothing with it, it seems intangible, ephemeral, and unreal. Yet it is only in this world, or better in this aspect of the total world, that true reality may be found. The world of things and objects is in itself inert and meaningless. It is always there ready to be analyzed, categorized, and organized by anyone who wishes to study it. It lets you use it this way whenever you wish, but it never gives itself to you. In the world of *I* and *Thou,* on the other hand, there is existence or being such as you possess, and on occasion, when you are given the grace to do so, you may meet another being and become bound up in relationship. Here you give yourself freely as the *Thou* you meet is given to you. When this happens, it is a very different thing from the mere observation of an object among the manifold objects in the world of your perception.

Examples of the world of I *and* Thou

Consider for example the astronomer who night after night is drawn to his vigil with the stars. Here, if we will let it, the twofold character of reality can emerge in all its contrast. For there is much more here to draw him than the mere cataloging, analyzing, and organizing of the stellar objects which appear to him for observation and study. True enough, this is the business which he as astronomer is about and the intended end product of his labor. But above and beyond all this there is, as he knows from past instances, the possibility of a meeting in which he as person may on occasion confront the remote portions of existence which he beholds so that he and they become bound up in relationship with each other and have in a sense to do with each other. It is only from such meetings that he has been able to discover that astronomy was meant for him and he for it. It is the possibility of their coming to him again which fills his heart with a strange excitement and lures him back with a potent charm to his nightly labors.

The botanist, William Seifriz, of the University of Pennsylvania tells a story of his graduate student days at Johns Hopkins which illuminates this twofold character of reality. He had been working on the technique of drawing out fine quartz fiber needles which could be used on a micromanipulator under a microscope to probe into living cells. One afternoon he caught an amoeba on the end of one of these needles and watched it excitedly as it put out long pseudopodia in one direction after another with the appearance of mortal struggle. In his excitement he called out to his major professor to come and see. "Look," he shouted, "he's trying to get away from me." He was roundly reprimanded by his professor for this unscientific slip and told he would never make a biologist if he talked that way about his observations. Only by treating the amoeba as an object with a certain structure and properties, and its motions under the stimulus of the needle as the necessary outcome of the physico-chemical reactions initiated by it could understanding be derived.

The professor was, of course, quite right. Science can deal only with objects and events, and the real amoeba has to be made over into an object of our perceptual experience in order to become a subject for biology. But for a moment the amoeba had become for Seifriz another being sharing in common with him the mystery of existence. In that moment these two beings had confronted each other across the intervening void and become bound up in relationship. In this event the world of *I* and *Thou* was revealed and the reality of the amoeba as a being, existing in the same way that *I* exist, emerged. Apart from such an event, the *I* in the world of *I* and *It* stands out in lonely elevation as the center of experience and knowledge, while the amoeba is reduced to the level of one of the manifold objects of the world which the *I* experiences and knows.

All of this applies even more clearly and decisively in the social sciences. In order for psychology or sociology to be operative at all, it is necessary that the persons under investigation first be transformed into objects. In psychology a human being is simply an observable object, an entity possessing a certain structure and behavior, alongside other entities such as rocks and trees, atoms and molecules, the sea, and the stars, which populate the perceivable world of the observer. This remains true even when the psychologist makes himself the object of his experimentation and investigation. The moment, however, that the psychologist as person confronts and really meets another person, face to face as it were, a new dimension is introduced which by its very nature cannot be a part of psychology since neither one in the relationship thus entered into is merely an object in the external world of the other.

The psychologist Carl R. Rogers of the University of Chicago has contrasted this dual role in the case of psychotherapy in a most illuminating way. Speaking of himself as scientist, he says:

> "In approaching the complex phenomena of therapy with the logic and methods of science, the aim is to work toward an *understanding* of the phenomena. In science this means an objective knowledge of events and of functional relationships between events. . . . If the scientific aim were fully achieved in this realm, we would presumably know that, in therapy, certain elements were associated with certain types of outcomes. . . . We could then very likely control outcomes of therapy by our manipulation of the elements contained in the therapeutic relationship."[2]

In contrast to this he describes the actual experience of therapy in the following way:

> "I launch myself into the therapeutic relationship having a hypothesis, or a faith, that my liking, my confidence, and my understanding of the other person's inner world, will lead to a significant process of becoming. I enter the relationship not as a scientist, not as a physician who can accurately diagnose and cure, but as a person, entering into a personal relationship. Insofar as I see him only as an object, the client will tend to become only an object. I risk myself, because if, as the relationship deepens, what develops is a failure, a regression, a repudiation of me and the relationship by the client, then I sense that I will lose myself, or a part of myself. At times this risk is very real, and is very keenly experienced. I let myself go into the immediacy of the relationship where it is my total organism which takes over and is sensitive to the relationship, not simply my consciousness. I am not consciously responding in a planful or analytic way. . . ."

[2] Rogers, Carl R., "Persons or Science? A Philosophical Question," *The American Psychologist,* vol. 10, 1955, pp. 267-278; also published in *Cross Currents,* vol. 3, 1953, pp. 289-306.

The absence of freedom in the world of I *and* It

It is only as we come to an awareness of this twofold character of reality that the ideas of freedom, destiny, and providence can acquire any content or meaning. They belong to the world of *I* and *Thou* as much as the ideas of chance, accident, and fate belong to the world of *I* and *It*. From the standpoint of science there is strictly speaking no such thing as freedom at all. For, on the one hand, there is the seat of experience and knowledge, the isolated *I*, which in the arbitrariness of its self-will desires this or that and plans and contrives for the achievement of its ends. On the other hand are the objects and events in the world around the *I* which are experienced and observed and which can be seen to be organized in a certain way and linked together in causally connected chains.

Where in all this is freedom to be found? If we look for it in the *I*, we might at first sight think to have found it in the arbitrariness of self-will. This seat of experience does seem to possess a certain sovereignty and autonomy. It has desires and a considerable amount of cleverness and ingenuity in attaining what it wants. It plans and contrives and makes use of the available means to bring its designs on the world to fruition. This certainly seems like freedom of the most sovereign and autonomous sort. Yet the moment the fatal question is asked, "What made me want this rather than that?" or "What made me do what I did rather than what I could so well have done otherwise?" then the illusion is dispelled. The *I*, too, is seen to be controlled by things and instincts, the product of its given heredity and environment. For even the *I* can be thought of as a possible object of experience and thus caught in the same network as the other objects which it manipulates and uses. The apparent freedom of the *I* which it seems to possess in the arbitrariness of its self-will is seen to be an illusion.

Suppose, then, we look for freedom among the objects of our experience. As we have seen in previous chapters, these are not, as science used to believe, rigorously determined. Throughout the natural order of things from electrons to people, we find alternative modes of response and the exercise of choice among them. Could it be that freedom resides here? Some indeed have thought to have found it there, as in the attempts to discover the basis for the freedom of the will in the Heisenberg principle of indeterminacy. But on closer inspection we find that these choices are always made at random in accordance with the requirements of probability. A choice to which a numerical probability is assigned is not the kind of thing at all that we have in mind when we speak of human freedom—the freedom for which we stand ready to sacrifice our lives if necessary to preserve it. As we have pointed out before, try as one will one cannot make anything more out of chance and accident in science than simply chance and accident.

As with freedom, so it is also with destiny and providence in the world of science, the world of *I* and *It*. On close inspection they, too, evaporate into nothingness. Here, however, there is a kind of substitute for destiny which clings tenaciously, especially among those who think about the larger problems of the world in scientific terms. It is really nothing more than the arbitrariness of self-will, but applied to mankind as a whole which tends to conceal its true character. It consists in the effort to persuade the human species that, now that it has somehow willy-nilly emerged out of the cosmic process, it is in a position, if it will only put its mind to it with an undivided determination, to take over the reins from the process which produced it and run things henceforth on its own terms. We shall have occasion to return to this illusion later in considerable detail. For the moment we need only remark that it is not the same thing as destiny at all, and that the arbitrariness of self-will does not, when applied to mankind as a whole, acquire a status different from that which it enjoys with the isolated individual.

Freedom emerges in relationship

It is only through entering into relationship that the meaning of freedom and destiny can be discovered. Only through real relationship can we be liberated from the bondage to the autonomous *I*. This is the only way in which we can, so to speak, get out of our skins and truly get at a reality which is not held off from us and made forever other than the *I* by the subject-object relation. The exercise of freedom is simply the exercise of the whole self in this elementary act of self-giving which liberates the self from the arbitrariness of its central position as the *I* which experiences and uses its world of *It*. Freedom is known as soon as we speak *Thou* to another being. This is known, for example, in the act of falling in love, and it is what we mean when we say that it is essential to the validity of marriage that both parties be completely free to contract it. It is also what the familiar Collect means when it says of the relation of the Christian to his Lord, "whose service is perfect freedom." When we understand freedom this way we see why it is that science should be so totally incapable of dealing with it. For it comes about only in the process of escaping from the subject-object relation to the world which science necessarily imposes on us.

Buber has described the free man in an especially eloquent passage:[3]

> "The free man is he who wills without arbitrary self-will. He believes in reality, that is, he believes in the real solidarity of the real twofold entity *I* and *Thou*. He believes in destiny, and believes that it stands in need of him. It does not keep him in leading-strings, it awaits him, he must go to it, yet does not know where it is to be found. But he knows that he must go out with his whole being. The matter will not turn out according to his decision; but what is to come will come only when he decides on what he is able to will. He must sacrifice his puny, unfree will, that is controlled by things and instincts, to his grand will, which quits defined for destined being. Then he intervenes no more, but at the same time he does not let things merely happen. He listens to what is emerging from himself, to the course of being in the world; not in order to be supported by it, but in order to bring it to reality as it desires, in its need of him, to be brought—with human spirit and deed, human life and death, I said *he believes,* but that really means *he meets.*"

Captivity to the world of I and It

It is possible for a man to live out his life without ever knowing freedom or destiny. All that is necessary is that he refuse to enter into relationship in order to preserve the autonomy and sovereignty of his *I*. Every *Thou* which points to him he refuses to meet, knowing that the meeting would lower the barricade and lose the autonomous self. To him the self-giving involved in saying "Thou" to another seems a threat, a loss of freedom as

[3] *Op. cit.,* p. 59.

he understands the word. What he imagines to be freedom is the arbitrariness of self-will, the preservation of the possible status in the world in which the alienated *I* occupies its unique position as the center which apprehends, manipulates, influences, and enjoys the world of things and events which is subjugated to the position of forever being only the object of the *I*'s experience. Often this is the case with the clever and successful man of action who alternately undertakes, negotiates, organizes, and exerts influence in the "outside" world of people and institutions, and then retreats "inside" to the privacy of his inner life where feelings and emotions are indulged and where his pleasure in his own success and cleverness can be enjoyed. For such a one freedom means nothing more than the illusion of autonomy and sovereignty which he enjoys in the arbitrariness of his own will, and there is simply no such thing as destiny and providence. The chances and accidents of life through which, to the free man, the hand of God in the shaping of events is revealed, are for him nothing more than his own good fortune or misfortune. How else could he regard them?

A remarkable recent book,[4] *The True Believer,* by Eric Hoffer provides a striking picture of the attractiveness of a life which is exclusively centered in itself. The book is remarkable because of the complete honesty of its thoroughgoing espousal of self-centeredness and its frank rejection of every conceivable entangling relationship, every proffered *Thou.* The author himself is a remarkable man who exemplifies in his own life the ideal which his book so forcefully promotes. Almost entirely self-taught through avid reading in public libraries, he worked as a migratory laborer for ten years after the depression and since

[4] Harper & Brothers, 1951.

then as a longshoreman on the West Coast, because as he says, "I knew . . . that I couldn't stand being dependent on the good graces of a boss." He never married and seems to have formed few if any close friendships. His book is written with suppressed anger and open scorn for all who give themselves to any movement or community, daemonic and divine alike, from a street corner gang to American democracy, or from Hitler to Christ. These are the "true believers" and Hoffer will have naught to do with any of them. A few scattered passages will serve to bring out the frankness and honesty with which he recognizes all the implications of his own preference for an autonomous existence:

> "The less justified a man is in claiming excellence for his own self, the more ready is he to claim all excellence for his nation, his religion, his race, or his holy cause."[5]
>
> "All forms of dedication, devotion, loyalty and self-surrender are in essence a desperate clinging to something which might give worth and meaning to our futile, spoiled lives."[6]
>
> "He who is free to draw conclusions from his individual experience and observation is not usually hospitable to the idea of martyrdom. For self-sacrifice is an unreasonable act. It cannot be the end-product of a process of probing and deliberating."[7]
>
> "We can be absolutely certain only about things we do not understand. A doctrine that is understood is shorn of its strength. Once we understand a thing, it is as if it had originated in us. And, clearly, those who are asked to renounce the self and sacrifice it cannot see eternal certitude in anything which originates in that self."[8]

[5] *Ibid.*, p. 14
[6] *Ibid.*, p. 15
[7] *Ibid.*, p. 78
[8] *Ibid.*, p. 79

"The chief preoccupation of an active mass movement is to instill in its followers a facility for united action and self-sacrifice, and . . . it achieves this facility by stripping each human entity of its distinctness and autonomy and turning it into an anonymous particle with no will and no judgment of its own."[9]

The reading of this book could form an excellent preparation for a deeper appreciation of the scope and profound meaning of the following continuation of the passage which we quoted earlier from Buber:

"The self-willed man does not believe and does not meet. He does not know solidarity of connexion, but only the feverish world outside and his feverish desire to use it. Use needs only to be given an ancient name, and it companies with the gods. When this man says *Thou,* he means 'O my ability to use,' and what he terms his destiny is only the equipping and sanctioning of his ability to use. He has in truth no destiny, but only a being that is defined by things and instincts, which he fulfils with the feeling of sovereignty—that is, in the arbitrariness of self-will. He has no grand will, only self-will, which he passes off as real will. He is wholly incapable of sacrifice, even though he may have the word on his lips; you know him by the fact that the word never becomes concrete. He intervenes continually, and that for the purpose of 'letting things happen.' Why should destiny, he says to you, not be given a helping hand? Why should the attainable means required by such a purpose not be utilised? He sees the free man, too, in this way; he can see him in no other. But the free man has no purpose here and means there, which he fetches for his purpose: he has only the one thing, his repeated decision to approach his destiny. He has made this decision, and from time to time, at every parting of ways, he will renew it. But he could sooner believe he was not alive than that the decision of his grand will was inadequate and

[9] *Ibid.,* p. 82

167

needed to be supported by a means. He believes; he meets. But the unbelieving core in the self-willed man can perceive nothing but unbelief and self-will, establishing of a purpose and devising of a means. Without sacrifice and without grace, without meeting and without presentness, he has as his world a mediated world cluttered with purposes. His world cannot be anything else, and its name is fate. Thus with all his sovereignty he is wholly and inextricably entangled in the unreal. He knows this whenever he turns his thoughts to himself; that is why he directs the best part of his spirituality to averting or at least to veiling his thoughts."[10]

The centrality of the covenant relationship in the Bible

It has been necessary to go to considerable length in contrasting the world of *I* and *It* with the world of *I* and *Thou,* because the recognition of this twofold character of reality is essential for a meaningful grasp of the Biblical idea of providence within the context of modern thought. The central core and heart of the Bible is an *I-Thou* relationship between a people and the living God, the old covenant between Israel and Yahweh, or the new covenant between Christ and His Church. This relationship is unique in kind and quality in human history. Formed first in the mists of pre-history between a group of coarse Bedouin nomads and the god of the volcano and the storm, it has persisted throughout the whole historic period to the present day. Out of the drama of this relationship God made Himself known ever more fully and deeply until this drama reached its stupendous climax in the central event of the Incarnation through which the process of revelation completed itself in Christ. It is as though out of all the peoples of the earth, God had entered into a mar-

[10] *Loc. cit.,* pp. 60, 61.

riage with one of them and revealed Himself to an extent which would not be possible outside the bond of the covenant; just as persons can reveal themselves fully only in the intimate personal bond of marriage. The people who lived out their whole history through victory and defeat, nationhood and exile, in this covenant with the living God came to know Him as no other people could. Their literature, the Bible, is their witness to this revelation and their record of the experience of living it throughout their history.

This one central fact of the Bible is prior to every other aspect. It is fruitless to attempt to arrive at the Biblical idea of providence apart from it. One must first come to know the living God as the Bible has revealed Him and be made a member of the household of God in His Church, sharing thereby in the covenant relationship with Him through Christ, before one can begin to discover His hand in the shaping of events as the Bible has seen it. We must come to know and believe "in the real solidarity of the real twofold entity *I* and *Thou*" in its Biblical fullness before Biblical providence can emerge as a reality of our own life and history.

The relation of providence to chance and accident

The realization of freedom and a sense of destiny, as Buber has so compellingly described it, is a common heritage of many peoples. God's revelation of Himself within the covenant is not an exclusive revelation. Just as a man may partially reveal himself to varying degrees in casual relationships with friends and associates but is able to do so fully only in an intimate and indissoluble bond such as marriage, so God has become known to some extent among all peoples but has revealed Himself fully only through Israel culminating in Christ. Corresponding to this gradation of revelation there is an associated gradation in the capacity to see His providential activity in the chances and accidents of history. So long as there is any relationship at all with Him there will be a sense of destiny. With increasing degrees of revelation one goes then all the way from an elementary, diffuse, and mostly hidden generalized sense of destiny to the fullness of providence in its Biblical sense, and to a recognition of the God who has revealed in Christ His love and mercy acting in judgment and redemption in history. Thus, what men generally speak of as destiny is the same kind of thing which the Bible knows as providence.

With these understandings established, we can see the decisive importance of Buber to our present problem. Buber is concerned to make manifest the range of reality which resides only in relationship for people who have become accustomed to think of reality only in terms of perceiving subjects and the objects and events of their experience. Our concern here is parallel though not identical to his, namely, to make manifest the truth and reality of Biblical providence for people who have become accustomed to think of history in scientific terms. The significance of Buber's penetrating insights for this purpose should now be evident. The difference between destiny and Biblical providence is one of degree only. They are qualitatively similar and, if we can find a way to understand one, there are no real barriers to an understanding of the other. When, however, we come to the difference between chance and accident as seen in science, and providence as seen in the Bible, we come upon a radical difference of an essential nature. It is here that the distinction which Buber reveals between the world of *I* and *It* and that of *I* and *Thou,* that is, between arbitrary self-will and fate on the one hand, and freedom and destiny on the other, is of crucial importance. It reveals to us in a decisive and illuminating way how and why it is that the methods of science can never penetrate beyond chance and accident to discover any evidence of providence, and at the same time how and why it should be that the hand of God in history can only be known, as the Church has always maintained, through revelation. Even more importantly this insight also shows us the basis for the strange circumstance which we have already noted in previous chapters, that one and the same sequence of events can be apprehended by one observer as merely a remarkable streak of luck while being recognized by another for what it really is: a mighty act of the living God. The reason is that the subject-object and person-person relationships are not two separate worlds but two aspects of a single total reality. Only it is possible for one to be imprisoned in the first so exclusively as not to know or experience the other at all.

Secular alternatives to providence

Looked at objectively from the standpoint solely of a dispassionate observer who is not involved in it and does not meet it, history is a necessarily random and chaotic affair. It is a vast and turbulent river which sweeps us along whether we will or no. The chances and accidents which fill it upset our plans and set our calculations at naught. It is filled with problems of such vastness and complexity that in the nature of things we can do nothing about them no matter how ingenious and skillful we may become. This is clearly the objective reality of history as viewed from the vantage point of the creature, man, within history.

Now it is significant that this objective view of the reality of history is tolerable only for those who share the Biblical understanding of providence. All others, and most notably the secular, scientifically oriented man of our day, find it so meaninglessly chaotic as to be intolerable. They find it necessary in order to go on living at all to hide this reality of history behind an illusion in which they are able to take heart and find hope. It will be our purpose now to explore the nature and origin of this secular illusion, and then to contrast with it the realism which is possible for the Christian in the same situation through the gifts of acceptance, humility, joy, and trust which he derives from his knowledge of the Lordship of Christ in history.

Secular man, by virtue of his slavery to scientific categories of thought about his world, seals himself off from any knowledge of or communion with the living God who has revealed Himself in Christ. He is isolated by this intellectual and spiritual imprisonment from all access to the living experience of His mighty power and sustaining providence. When, therefore, he considers man as he can be observed in history, he sees only what is objectively apparent about him from the standpoint of a perceiving subject capable of observing him. That is, he sees him as one among many biological species which has emerged at the end of a tremendously long and involved sequence of remarkable and certainly unrepeatable chances and accidents made up of random molecular associations in a changing physical environment. Were it not for the further accident that he happens to be a member of this species, so that its welfare and future matter to him, he would be able simply to let the matter rest there as being really all in fact that can be said on the subject in an objective way. But since the one who has observed this fact about the species man is himself as observer also a man, he cannot let the matter rest there. To do so would be intolerable.

At this juncture the illusion which he generates to hide the reality which has been objectively apprehended is itself a striking example of the barrier which separates the *I* from the *It*. For the required illusion is found not in the objective world of the *It* at all, but within the subjective world of the *I*. It is indeed simply an appropriation to the species as a whole of the autonomy and sovereignty which is the characteristic of the isolated *I*. Just as the *I* can arbitrarily will what it wishes and set about to use the world in which it is immersed for the fulfillment of its desires, so, too, perhaps man in history can arbitrarily set himself a goal and set about to master history to the service of his goal. That is the illusion which secular man summons up out of the depths of his own autonomy to conceal the reality of his objective status, and give him an alternative to providence on which he can pin his hopes.

Let us examine a few specific examples of the way in which this illusion is created and used to hide the human predicament as it is objectively known in science. The anthropologist, V. Gordon Childe, has developed it through the story of "man's progress through the ages" in a book under the astounding title, from a strictly scientific standpoint, *Man Makes Himself*.[11] It is described on the cover as "An authoritative and inspiring history of the rise of civilization, including the nineteen major contributions through which men have achieved mastery of their

[11] One of the series of Mentor Books, published by the New American Library, New York, 1951.

environment." Professor Childe is confident not only that man is in a position to create for himself whatever kind of world he may, in the arbitrariness of his self-will, determine to have, but even more surprisingly that he has already achieved mastery over his environment! He is one of many who look back over the whole course of human history as though it were a record of achievements purposely planned and brought about by human ingenuity and foresight in order to persuade us to put our whole trust and confidence in ourselves. The implication seems to be that he means for us to believe that man intended all along that his history should come out the way it has. How else could man be in the process of making himself? It is, however, only necessary to examine the literature of each age in each culture to establish the clear truth of the fact that history has never turned out the way the men who lived it expected or intended it to. The fact is, of course, that man can neither predict nor design his destiny, and that what he has become so far in his history is, objectively considered, the result of a miraculous streak of good luck threading through a maze of chances and accidents. Such a conclusion is, however, clearly intolerable and so secular man conceals the truth of it by trying to believe in spite of the clear evidence of history that man really can master his fate and make the future what he wills it to be. Even so eminent a figure as Mr. Bernard Baruch has been quoted as saying, "I have no economic radar to penetrate the future, but we can make it what we will it to be. Of that I am sure."[12]

The evolutionist G. G. Simpson, whom we quoted in an earlier chapter, calls us to this same hope in the following words: "Man has risen, not fallen. He can choose to develop his capaci-

[12] Quoted in *Science,* vol. 121, March 25, 1955, p. 408.

ties as the highest animal and to try to rise still farther, or he can choose otherwise. The choice is his responsibility, and his alone. There is no automatism that will carry him upward without choice or effort and there is no trend solely in the right direction. Evolution has no purpose; man must supply this for himself."[13]

The physiologist, Homer W. Smith, puts the same hope in a way which brings out even more clearly the arbitrariness of self-will which this view of man's role in history entails:

> "He who has purposes and plans must make a choice, no other can make it for him. A proper view of man finds no place for a priori 'should' or 'ought' or any categorical imperative, but only for this: that if a man so acts, that is *his* action, and his alone. . . . History . . . reveals that man does not need any brand of transcendental metaphysics—his lasting contentments and achievements he has found wholly within the frame of reference that takes things as they are in the here and now. No pattern of living is written in the stars: each may be tried and esteemed according to the individual."[14]

In his presidential address to the Eighth International Congress of Genetics in 1948 on the subject, "Genetics in the Scheme of Things," the geneticist, H. J. Muller, calls for similar reliance in man's capacity to direct the course of events towards his objectives. Here, however, an attempt is made to soften some of the arbitrariness of the goal which man might set for himself. Speaking of the need of modern men and women for a sense of meaning and direction in life, he says:

> "Just this can be obtained, in a really rational way, with the help of the long view of genetics, when they contemplate the

[13] *Op. cit.*, p. 310.
[14] Smith, Homer W., *Man and His Gods,* Little, Brown, 1956, pp. 441-443.

unparalleled epic struggles of their ancestral threads of life, multiplying, transforming, sacrificing, weaving, and interweaving through the ages, to the stage of those marvelous organizations which are represented by themselves and their fellows, and when they realize, further, that this is still in process, but with far greater possibilities than before, provided they now prove themselves worthy enough to take over the reins from the genes, whose task in furnishing the directives by the process of mere trial and error is at last done, and to steer for themselves henceforth towards a future of ever greater undestanding and achievement, in a spirit of increasing fellowship and love."[15]

This passage together with the arguments leading up to it stands in some contrast with the others in several respects. First, we note a certain sense of destiny which pervades it, particularly with respect to the major period of history prior to the point at which man has taken over the reins. Secondly, the formation of the goal toward which we are to work together is expressed without the stark arbitrariness of Simpson and Smith, and it is given a Christian form, although, of course, without any of the substance which undergirds Christianity. Earlier in this same address he grapples at some length with the arbitrariness of self-will which he realizes clearly to be involved. This is done in an interesting and illuminating manner. First, he notes that we are what we are because of our genes and that these have been given to us as a result of the long and complex process through which the genes evolved. Thus, as he expresses it, our genes represent a certain set of interests whose partial fulfillment at this stage of history we represent. If now we are to take over from the genes and substitute our interests for theirs for the remainder of the

[15] *Proceedings of the Eighth International Congress of Genetics,* Lund, 1948, p. 126; published as a supplement to *Hereditas.*

process, does this not represent a certain degree of presumption? We are, he points out, all aware that this is not "the best of all possible worlds" nor we its "best conceivable inhabitants." In taking over the reins from the genes, therefore, we must try to decide what we mean by "best," as well as whether our interests and the interests of the genes which produced us are opposed to each other.

After considerable argument with himself he decides two things which, from the standpoint of our concern here with the arbitrariness of self-will, might be expressed in the following way. First, it would seem that our interests and the genes' are likely to be common ones because they were responsible for producing us the way we are so that anything we arbitrarily agree upon is likely in the end to have really been determined by them anyhow. Second, it would also seem that there is sufficient ground for the objectives of understanding and love to make these worthy goals even if they have to be arbitrarily chosen. These conclusions illuminate quite strikingly the problem which the self faces in the world of *I* and *It* in endeavoring to escape from the prison of its own arbitrariness and find a reality which is not contingent on itself. For otherwise whatever reality there is, no matter how worthy or noble it may be, dies with the self and is swallowed up in meaninglessness.

The central theme of Muller's solution is, however, the same as the others which we have quoted. It is, namely, that man in his autonomy and sovereignty is quite capable of mastering fate and directing history to whatever goal he chooses for it. The shaping of events by chance and accident is, he believes, over, since, as he says, the direction of the cosmic process by mere trial and error is at last done. Now at last man can seize the reins and direct the process in a really rational way, provided only that men can somehow get together and decide on a common goal and even more importantly that we can somehow convince ourselves that the goal we have chosen is not really arbitrary.

It should be clear by now that all such proposals are essentially illusory. Their illusory character rests on two fundamental defects, one of which arises out of the nature of history itself, and the other out of the inescapable character of the world of *I* and *It*. The role of chance and accident in events is not, as we have adequately demonstrated from science itself, at an end at all. Man, therefore, deludes himself when he hopes to master history, not because he merely lacks sufficient ingenuity and cleverness for the task, but because the nature of history itself makes it fundamentally uncontrollable by man. With respect to the other defect, we have already seen the dilemmas which confront the self in its efforts to get outside of itself. So long as the new dimension *I-Thou* remains unknown, efforts will be made to construct some system of values and some framework of meaning within the world of *I* and *It* in such a way as to mask the arbitrariness which arises from the fact that the *I* in its isolation can do nothing else but decide upon what it wishes to will. Every such effort is, however, doomed to failure at the outset. The only escape from the burden of maintaining an autonomous existence in an alien world lies through the discovery of a new dimension which opens up when true freedom is exercised and destiny is met.

The gifts of providence

In contrast to these secular alternatives to providence stands the reality of providence itself and the character which life acquires when it is truly and freely lived under the Lordship of the living God. There are several gifts of priceless value which come with the acquisition of the capacity so to live. Among these are the gifts of humility, trust, and greatness. We can do no better by way of concluding this book than to survey these gifts of providence and attempt to bring out their nature and worth.

Among these gifts the most crucial and transforming in the life of man is the gift of true Christian humility. Given this virtue, life becomes a lovely adventure even in the midst of tribulation. Without it, life can only be an increasingly frustrating and terrifying journey as the burden of maintaining a continuous record of successful intervention among the chances and accidents of an inscrutable history becomes crushing under the stern realities of the objective world. There are innumerable aspects of the world and the shaping of its history about which, in the nature of things, we can do nothing. True humility is simply the recognition and acceptance of this primary reality of our finite status in creation. But secular man does not dare admit to any such predicament. How can he? In a world without God there is no one beside man left to cope with the world. To him humility is nothing short of an act of defeat, a giving up of the struggle. He can see in it nothing beyond an unnecessary self-imposed resignation, a forfeiture of man's right to use and change the world as he thinks best, and an attitude of submission which sits back and merely lets things happen. He cannot see it in any other way.

But he who shares in the reality of the Judeo-Christian insight into history as an expression of the providence of God acting both in judgment and in redemption sees the whole matter in a new light. He knows that the service of his Lord does not involve any denial or curtailment of his freedom, but rather its release and fulfillment. Providence does not bind you and lead you about on its apron strings. Rather it comes forth to meet you, as you to it. The Lordship of Christ in history is not a detached principle of explanation like the law of gravity, but a triumpant and glorious hope. Life in a world which is consciously apprehended as the expression of the will of its Creator is not a sequence of baleful incidents thwarting human purposes, but a meaningful and joyous adventure. The recognition of providence in the chances and accidents of the tumultuous unfolding of events converts what otherwise can only seem the dark fruition of an inscrutable fate into the smiling face of destiny. To be sure, he who knows providence can no longer sustain the proud autonomy which strives to master history. But he is not thereby cast down and trodden under foot by an overwhelming and alien power. Quite the contrary. Rather does he find himself liberated from the unrelenting demands of the isolated autonomous self, and freed at last to go forth and meet life in ever-ripening fulfillment. Providence replaces the proud arrogance of achievement with the trusting humility of true greatness.

This is really the way it is also with science as a human activity, as opposed to science as a body of knowledge about the world. Science as it is actually carried out by those with a real love for their work is anything but a cold and calculating enterprise for the subjection or mastery of an inert nature. It is rather a warm and thrilling adventure with a deep sense of meaning and fulfillment about it. The typical scientist is a person of great humility and humanity with a profound sense of being called to his task and an inner conviction that it was meant for him, and he for it. He does not know where it will lead him, but he would sooner believe he was not alive than that it could in any wise lead him wrongly. For him the mysterious world in which man finds himself is meant to be known and apprehended as fully and richly as may prove possible. To tell him he must change or redirect his efforts because further knowledge in a given direction might reveal frightening and unwanted potentialities in the world which it is our lot to inhabit, seems to him not only presumptuous but downright blasphemous. His calling in life is to understand ever more deeply and fully. Even though he may have lost all direct association with the Judeo-Christian heritage, he has enough vestigial reminiscence of its sense of providence left in him to know that this is what he is meant for and that in it lies his fulfillment.

The gift of humility and trust which the Biblical recognition of providence confers is a great puzzle to secular man. He who is clothed with true Christian humility is anything but resigned. Through his trust in his Lord, he believes in destiny and in its need of him, and he is constantly alert and ready to meet it. Things happen to him all the time, but he does not merely let them happen; he awaits them expectantly and welcomes them when they come. He is not out to upset or change the world, but he rejoices in wonder and gratitude at the changes in it which come through him. You can tell him by the joy that lives within him, and the absence of the strains and tensions and anxieties which mark those who must always be intervening in order that things may come out according to some plan. You can tell him, too, by his utter realism. He takes the world as it is along with the littleness of men within it. In his humble recognition of the impotence of his own powers, he does not see how he would be able to accomplish anything at all; yet you always find him praising God for the great things that are accomplished through him. History continues to be for him as profound a mystery as it is for the non-Christian, but it is never inscrutable or alien. It is charged with meaning and filled with destiny, and he glories in his participation in it. Since, however, he has no idea of trying to master or control history, he is neither optimistic nor pessimistic about it. Instead he simply believes in it with a sure trust and a living hope. That in which he is involved will not turn out according to his expectations, but time after time he is amazed to find that greater things have come from his involvement than he could ever have imagined or hoped for.

Closely allied with the gift of humility is the gift of greatness. In the world of *I* and *It* where the *I* reigns in the arbitrariness of self-will and simply experiences and uses the objective world in which it is immersed, there cannot be any such thing as greatness. There can be ingenuity, competence, prudence, good fortune, and success; but not greatness. There are many famous men whom we do not naturally think of as great men. The elements which go to make up this distinction are very much the same as those which distinguish self-will from true freedom and they arise in the same way from the twofold aspect of the world as *I* and *It* or as *I* and *Thou*. It is illuminating in this respect to contrast Napoleon and Lincoln, both of whom were indeed famous but only one of whom is commonly referred to as great.

The prototype of all true greatness is found in the Biblical figure of Abraham. In the picture of this lonely figure stepping forth from his homeland into the unknown for a meeting with destiny which could not be foreseen but only awaited, as well as in all the subsequent events which befell him, we find the

Biblical insight into the reality of providence made concrete and evident. Here, too, the real meaning of freedom is made manifest along with that of providence with the clarity which comes from great simplicity. Once we have come to see in Abraham the epitome of the Biblical meaning of freedom and providence, we can find in him, too, a central example of the gifts of humility, trust, and greatness which are bestowed on all who, out of the depths of their freedom, find the grace to respond in full commitment to the living God who governs all things both in heaven and earth.

INDEX

Date Due

DEC 7 '66			
NOV			
DEC 3 '66			
MT. UNION			
JAN 1 8 1973			
	PRINTED	IN U. S. A.	